# Morse Code

## for Radio Amateurs

*12th Edition*

*by*

**Roger Cooke**, G3LDI

Radio Society of Great Britain

Published by the Radio Society of Great Britain, 3 Abbey Court, Fraser Road, Priory Business Park, Bedford MK44 3WH. Tel 01234 832700 www.rsgb.org

Book first published as 'Morse Code for the Radio Amateur' 1947

This 12th edition first published 2016

Reprinted 2017

ISBN: 9781 9101 9319 8

Layout and Edited by: Mike Browne, G3DIH

Cover Design: Kevin Williams, M6CYB

Production: Mark Allgar, M1MPA

Printed in Great Britain by Latimer Trend & Company Ltd. of Plymouth

# Contents

# Foreword

I first became fascinated by Morse Code and Short Wave when tuning around on my Dad's Murphy radio set on the Short Waves. I followed the normal route into amateur radio for those days, the 1950s, with the RAE and a mandatory Morse test. The Morse test has since been abolished in the UK, but Morse is still an enormous part of the hobby.

The GB2CW scheme has been rejuvenated and is now used widely over the UK. Learning the code and attaining a level of proficiency is still down to the individual however, and perseverance and lots of practice is needed.

The purpose of this book is to encourage you to follow that path and enjoy the huge satisfaction of using Morse on the air, in DX-ing, rag-chewing, contesting or whatever your interest is. Nobody said it was easy, but then nothing worthy of achievement is attained without effort! I hope this book helps you to enjoy Morse as much as I do.

*Roger J. Cooke*, G3LDI

*March 2016*

# Chapter 1

# The Morse Code and its History

Morse Code is a method of representing letters, numbers and punctuation marks by means of a code signal sent intermittently. It was developed by Samuel Morse and Alfred Vail in 1835. "Morse Code" is essentially a way to represent the letters of the alphabet using patterns of long and short pulses. A unique pattern is assigned to each character of the alphabet, as well as to the ten numerals, and four punctuation marks, period, comma, slash and question mark. These long and short pulses are translated into electrical signals by an operator using a telegraph key, and the electrical signals are translated back into the alphabetic characters by a skilled operator at the distant receiving instrument. It has also been acknowledged that Morse's partner Alfred Vail very likely assisted in the development of the code and the instruments used to transmit and receive it.

Morse code is an early form of digital communications, something that is common-place today. However, unlike modern binary digital codes that use just two states (commonly represented as 1 and 0), it uses five: dot (·), dash (–), short gap (between each letter), medium gap (between words) and a long gap (between phrases or sentences, not often applied). Of course, Morse code is also a binary code, in that it is based on only two states on and off. Both views (dits/dahs/spaces vs. on and off) are correct.

Samuel Finley Breese Morse, **Fig 1.1**, was born in 1791, at Charlestown, Massachusetts. His father was a Congregational minister and a scholar of high standing, who, by careful management, was able to send his three sons to Yale College. Samuel (or Finley, as he was called by his family) attended at the age of fourteen and came under the influence of Benjamin Silliman, Professor of Chemistry, and of Jeremiah Day, Professor of Natural Philosophy, afterwards President of Yale College, whose teaching gave him impulses which in later years led to the invention of the telegraph. "Mr Day's lectures are very interesting," the young student wrote home in 1809, "they are upon electricity; he has given us some very fine experiments, the whole class

*Fig 1.1: Samuel Morse*

taking hold of hands form the circuit of communication and we all receive the shock apparently at the same moment." Electricity, however, was only an alluring study. It afforded no means of livelihood, and Morse had gifts as an artist; in fact, he earned a part of his college expenses painting miniatures at five dollars apiece. He decided, therefore, that art should be his vocation. However, he found it a very difficult and impecunious profession. He also taught art to supplement his income. One enthusiastic student who had little money for his art course paid $10 as a part payment for his course. This is what Samuel Morse said:

"This is my first meal for twenty-four hours. Strother, don't be an artist. It means beggary. Your life depends upon people who know nothing of your art and care nothing for you. A house dog lives better, and the very sensitiveness that stimulates an artist to work keeps him alive to suffering."

## Locust Grove

The main house at Locust Grove is a villa in the Italianate style designed in 1850 for artist and inventor Samuel F. B. Morse by architect Alexander Jackson Davis. Fifty years later the house was renovated and expanded for new owners William and Martha Young. Their daughter, Annette Innis Young, eventually created the foundation that preserves the Estate as a museum today. **Fig 1.2** shows a picture of the house.

While no furnishings survive from the Morse family's years at Locust Grove, the Museum Pavilion is the home of a permanent exhibit that explores Samuel Morse's two careers, first as an artist and later as the inventor of the telegraph and Morse Code.

*Fig 1.2: Locust Grove*

Original works of art, including portraits, landscapes, drawings and sculpture from all phases of his career illustrate the range of his talent. In the Telegraph Gallery, reproductions of Morse's early telegraph models introduce visitors to the electromagnetic telegraph.

Overlooking the Hudson River, the estate is open to visitors and would be very worthwhile taking time to view. It is situated in Poughkeepsie, New York. Read all about it at:

*http://www.lgny.org/the-mansion*

## The Birth of the Telegraph

In 1836 Morse took into his confidence one of his colleagues in the University, Leonard D Gale, who assisted him greatly, in improving the telegraph invention, while the inventor himself formulated the rudiments of the telegraphic alphabet, or Morse code, as it is known today. At length all was ready for a test and the message flashed from transmitter to receiver. The telegraph was born, though only an infant as yet.

Morse concentrated more on his electrical experiments and on the 2nd September 1837, a successful experiment was made with seventeen hundred feet of copper wire coiled around the room. This was in the presence of Alfred Vail (*see* **Fig 1.3**), a student whose family owned the Speedwell Iron Works at Morristown, New Jersey.

*Fig 1.3: Alfred Vail*

Vail at once took an interest in the invention and persuaded his father, Judge Stephen Vail, to advance money for experiments. Samuel Morse filed a petition for a patent in October and admitted his colleague Gale, as well as Alfred Vail, to partnership. Experiments followed at the Vail shops, all the partners working day and night in their enthusiasm. The apparatus was then brought to New York and gentlemen of the city were invited to the University to see it work before it left for Washington.

The equipment was gradually improved and was demonstrated in 1837. He eventually applied for a patent in 1840. A line was set up between Baltimore and Washington and the first message, sent on 24 May, 1844, was: "What hath God wrought!" The original keyer, if you can call it that, or telegraph is shown in **Fig 1.4** but I don't think many modern amateurs would want one in the shack.

Morse's original code consisted of combinations of dots and dashes that represented numbers. Each number represented a word. This required looking up the number in a book to find the word it represented. A telegraph key was then used to tap out the sequence of dots, dashes, and pauses that represented the number.

*Fig 1.4: First telegraph model (c.1835) made from an old artist canvas stretcher, home-made battery and wooden clockworks.*
*Code was generated by the wooden arm riding across the metal saw tooth dies representing dots and dashes and printed out on the paper tape move by the clockworks*

Although Morse invented the telegraph, he lacked technical expertise. He entered an agreement with Alfred Vail who built more practical equipment. Vail developed a system in which each letter or symbol is sent individually, using combinations of dots, dashes, and pauses. Morse and Vail agreed that Vail's method of representing individual symbols would be included in Morse's patent. This system, known as American Morse code, was the version that was used to transmit the first telegraph message. The receiving apparatus is shown in **Fig 1.5**.

The code may be transmitted as an audio tone, a steady radio signal switched on and off (only the carrier wave, or CW, also known as continuous wave), an electrical pulse down a telegraph wire, or as a mechanical or visual signal (e.g. a flashing light).

*Fig 1.5: Morse/Vailtelegraph register, 1844. This register was used to receive the message "What Hath God Wrought" on the experimental circuit between Washington DC, and Baltimore, Maryland*

## American Morse Code

American Morse differs from International Morse in eleven letters, in all of the numerals except the number '4', and in the punctuation code. The unit of the code is the dot, representing a very brief depression of the telegraph key. The dash represents a depression lasting three times as long as a dot. Between the depressions there is a pause equal in time to one dot, except in a few letters and signs, when there is a wait of two dots. The pause between letters in a word lasts as long as one dash, between words it lasts as long as two dashes.

This code is virtually extinct, and no longer in commercial use. American Morse Code, sometimes referred to as "Railroad Morse" uses a slightly different structure of dots and dashes and uniquely spaces also to represent numbers, letters, and special characters. This style of Morse code was developed for land operators working over telegraph wire rather than via radio signals. It is most frequently seen today in railroad museums and American civil war re-enactments. There are still some old timers around who can use both. Dick Bendicksen, N7ZL, who died in 2006 aged 87, could send and receive at 40WPM using both code sets. That feat takes real skill and is quite extraordinary! To compare the two codes look at **Fig 1.6**.

The Morse code was developed so that operators could translate the indentations marked on the paper tape into text messages. The shorter marks were called 'dots', and the longer ones 'dashes', and the letters most commonly used in the English language were assigned the shortest sequences.

In the original Morse telegraphs, the receiver's armature made a clicking noise as it moved into and out of position for marking the tape. Operators soon learned to read the clicks directly as the beginning and end of dots and dashes, meaning

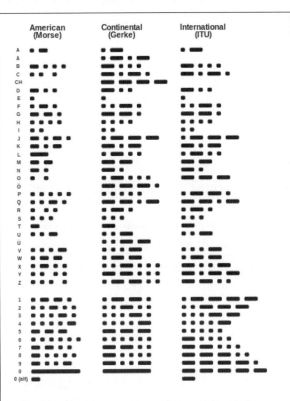

Comparison of historical versions of Morse code with the current standard.
1. American Morse code as originally defined.
2. The modified and rationalised version used by Gerke on German railways.
3. The current ITU standard.

*Fig 1.6*: *Comparison of historical versions of Morse code with the current standard*

that it was no longer necessary to use the tape. This older style of code was developed to accommodate the way in which operators listened to Morse code sent to them. Rather than hearing tones from a speaker or headphones as we do now using International Morse Code, in the earliest days of telegraphy one would hear two clicks from a mechanical sounding device for each key movement. Pressing the key makes a click, and releasing the key makes a clack. Thus, each key movement, up or down was uniquely heard. In this mechanical sounder system, an A:

( •— ) would sound like: clickClack click - - - Clack.

When Morse code was adapted to radio, the dots and dashes were normally sent as short and long tones. It was later found that people become more proficient at receiving Morse code when it is taught as a language that is heard, instead of one read from a page. To reflect the sound of Morse code, practitioners vocalise a dash as 'dah', and a dot as a 'dit'. When a dit is not the final element of a character, its sound is shortened to "di-" to maintain a better vocal rhythm. For instance, the letter F:

( ••—• ) is 'di-di-dah-dit'.

This older style of code was developed to accommodate the way in which operators listened to Morse code sent to them. This is quite different from "CW" code where beeps are heard for as long as the key is engaged. The term LID, meaning a poor operator, comes from those operators who could not read the clicks and clacks, so they put a tobacco tin lid on the sounder to make it easier!

## Modern International Morse Code

The Modern International Morse Code was invented by Friedrich Clemens Gerke in 1848 and used for the telegraphy between Hamburg and Cuxhaven in Germany. After some minor changes in 1865 it was standardised at the International Telegraphy congress in Paris(1865), and later accepted by the ITU as International Morse Code.

International Morse code is still in use today, albeit not in the commercial world. It has become almost exclusively the province of amateur radio operators. Until 2003 the International Telecommunications Union (ITU) mandated Morse code proficiency as part of the amateur radio licensing procedure throughout the world. In the amateur radio world, certain parts of the amateur radio bands are still reserved for transmission of Morse code signals only.

Since Morse relies on only an (on-off keyed) radio signal, it requires less complex equipment than other forms of radio communication, and it can be used in very high noise / low signal environments. It also requires less bandwidth than voice communications, typically 100-150Hz.

The extensive use of pro-signs, Q codes, and restricted format of typical messages facilitates communication between amateur radio operators who do not share a common mother tongue and would have great difficulty in communicating using voice modes.

## Historical use of Morse

Morse code has played its very important part in history. Some of the well known uses include radio rooms on ocean liners. Remember the R.M.S Titanic's SOS distress call in 1912. What does SOS really mean? - "Save Our Ship". Before the year 1912, ships at sea used the Morse code distress signals "CQD", which means, "Call To Quarters - Danger!" As you can see, a few letters transmitted in International Morse code make it possible for effective conversation between operators of different nations. The radio operators as they were then, highly qualified Morse operators, have disappeared. A typical navy radio room is shown in **Fig 1.7**.

The receiver on the table is a model SE-1220 (a long-wave version of the SE-143). Atop the receiver is a model SE-1387 RF Driver (a single tube RF amplifier used to improve the receiver's sensitivity).

To the right of this unit is a group of honeycomb coils, probably of DeForest manufacture. At the far right is what is most likely a vacuum tube detector unit.

Equipment bearing the "SE" designation were built by or for the U.S. Navy's Bureau of Steam Engineering. This organization was assigned the responsibility for developing radio equipment for the fleet, and was later to become the Naval Research Laboratory (NRL). Several spare Morse keys can be seen on the shelf at the left of the picture. There are still Naval Coastal stations active on the air now. One such is K6KPH. The web site is well worth a visit:

*Fig 1.7: A typical navy radio room*

http://radiomarine.org/gallery/show?keyword=K6KPH&panel=pab1_3

Morse was in constant use all through WW2 as well, and during that war, codes and ciphers were used to try to deter the enemy from receiving the information being trans-

*Fig 1.8*: A row of HRO receivers

mitted. The most notorious and highly complex encoding was employed in the well-known Enigma machine, first invented by Arthur Scherbius in 1918 and employed in the business world. The military took over the Enigmas and used them for wartime traffic. These messages were encoded and sent in Morse. The secret listening station at Bletchley Park was set up to receive and decode these messages. They used the ubiquitous HRO receivers, **Fig 1.8** showing the row of HRO receivers with trained operators at each one copying the coded groups. These were then passed to the deciphering operators and eventually this led to the cracking of the codes used in the Enigma machines. It's really good to know that the use of Morse code in this way helped to shorten WW2 by several years. I always find it very inspiring to visit Bletchley and know just what happened there. This picture was taken by Colin Page G0TRM. Other pictures from Bletchley can be found on the CARS web site at:

*http://www.g0mwt.org.uk/events/bletchley-park-2010/bletchley.htm*

Amateur radio operators were also used in the field as "Secret Listeners" as they were called, all because of their superior Morse Code receiving ability.

Morse was also used in aeroplanes, navigators had to send and receive Morse, and so did the land forces, so it was a Code that was used globally for many years by all.

## Outdated Mode?

It is considered outdated by some, mostly those that cannot use it and that is mostly because they cannot be bothered to use it. Most of us that had to take a mandatory Morse test still use it today, and in fact it is those that are among the most experienced amateur operators, hence the need to pass on that skill to the coming generations of amateurs, and not let it be allocated to the shelves of history.

Morse code's descendants and other newer digital modes have superseded Morse code, with the argument that newer 'high-tech' modes using computers are easier and faster to use. While it may be true that picking up a telephone is much simpler than having to train people in Morse code to transmit a message, there is the argument that technology is good only if technology is working. Morse code's simplicity has often been able to overcome technological problems. Military and civilian emergency communications specialists have pointed out that even if a high-tech voice, picture, or data-transmitting device is malfunctioning and can produce only pulsed static, it can still effectively relay a coherent message if it is used to produce and send Morse code.

Theoretically a low keying speed occupies a small bandwidth, so that 12WPM will fit comfortably into a bandwidth of a few tens of Hertz. This does not quite work in practice. Even so, the ability to use narrow band filters - 250Hz typically - enables far more CW stations to occupy a given bandwidth, plus there is a greater tolerance of interference.

Morse code is also very popular among QRP operators for enabling very long distance, low-power communication. Readability can be sustained by trained operators even though the signal is only faintly readable. This level of "penetration" is due to the fact that all transmitted energy is concentrated in a very small bandwidth making the use of a narrow receiver bandwidth practical. A narrow bandwidth receiver uses filters to exclude interference on frequencies close to the desired frequency. Concentrating the transmitted energy in a small bandwidth gives the signal a "spectral brightness" that is much higher than the average natural noise.

EME (Moonbounce) communications frequently use Morse despite the emergence of purpose-designed digital modes. Handling extremely weak signals bounced off the surface of the Moon makes Morse a useful mode. There is also much more satisfaction in using one's brain to read a message from a weak signal, rather than see a message appear on a computer screen from a signal that might be in or even below the noise threshold.

High speed Morse is used in meteor scatter contacts on VHF. Reflection from the ionised trail of meteors lasts only a few seconds so speeds of several hundred words per minute are used. This is generated and decoded by computer, enabling communication to be established. Usually this is by pre-arranged skeds with each station transmitting on alternate 15-second intervals. However, it is still using Morse code.

Conversely, 136kHz operators achieve long distances by using extremely slow Morse with each dot several seconds (sometimes up to two minutes) long, usually readable on a computer screen as the only way of deciphering the message.

Most DXpeditions use CW and some even favour it exclusively. If you chase DX or IOTA Islands, CW should be one of your prime modes. It is far from out-dated, but does not form part of the HF requirements in this modern age.

Fifty years ago, most amateurs operated CW only because to operate telephony it was necessary to have a modulator. Not only that, but in those days it was mandatory to spend the first year on CW anyway. It is this generation of dyed in the wool CW operators that are keen to perpetuate the mode. There are still a large number of CW only contests too and we need to maintain interest in the mode and train newcomers to become proficient operators. There is nothing quite like sitting on the CW end of 20 meters with headphones on, and tuning across conversations, chatting with friends and breaking the pile-up on a DXpedition! It's a fascinating and skilful world of its own.

## References

[1] *http://www.lgny.org/the-mansion*

[2] *http://radiomarine.org/gallery/show?keyword=K6KPH&panel=pab1_3*

— • — • •••• • — • — — • — • • — •    •• — — —

# Chapter 2

# Morse and the Radio Amateur

RADIO AMATEURS have been associated with the Morse code ever since the hobby started. The two are synonymous and the quintessential picture of a radio amateur is one of him sitting in front of radio equipment with headphones on pounding a Morse key.

However, the modern Morse code enthusiast will be found using an electronic keyer and paddle plus a computer as shown in the picture of a field day contest station in **Fig 2.1**. The paddle is there for comments etc., but the keyboard is used mostly for contesting these days.

*Fig 2.1*: Paul Cort-wright G3SEM operating at Norfolk ARC National Field Day, using both an electronic keyer and a computer

The old image has faded somewhat in the last few years, mainly due to newcomers to the hobby not having to learn Morse at all. Indeed a lot of newly licenced amateurs openly admit they have no interest at all in Morse and won't use it. However, listen on HF during a contest or to a pile-up calling a DX-pedition and you will find that it really is still as popular as it was.

You will still find amateurs licensed in the 1940s through to the 1980s using Morse, and some licensed after that of course. However, new licensees do not have to be able to read Morse. There is no longer a mandatory Morse test. In the UK, it has been replaced by a Morse assessment (**Fig 2.2**)with the idea that it might perhaps encourage some to use the mode after having received a licence.

Some people have no desire at all to use Morse, but by not using the code they are virtually excluded from 40% of the HF bands. The RSGB Cumulative short contests have sparked a renewed interest in Morse.

**Fig 2.2**: *Morse Proficiency Certificate*

In the United States until 1991, a demonstration of the ability to send and receive Morse code at five words per minute (5WPM) was required to receive an FCC amateur radio licence. Demonstration of this ability is still required for the privilege to use the HF bands. Until 1999, proficiency at the 20WPM level was required to receive the highest level of amateur license (Extra Class). As of 15 April, 2000, the FCC reduced the Extra Class requirement to 5WPM.

The World Radiocommunication Conference of 2003 (WRC-03) made optional the international Morse code requirement for amateur radio licensing. Although the requirement remains on the books in the US, Canada, and elsewhere, some countries are working to eliminate the requirement entirely.

## Benefits of the Morse Code

One of the main benefits of using Morse is that it makes the most efficient use of the bandwidth available, as discussed in Chapter 1. It is possible to have ten CW contacts in the space that one SSB signal would occupy. It is also ideal for low power operation, and is a great mode for the beginner.

It is also the only mode that requires a practical skill by the operator to create the means of communication, and is an art form in itself. Morse operators take a great pride in their skill, much like a musician. It also enables the operator to use the hobby quietly without making a lot of noise in the house, and it is possible to improve one's speed, regardless of what level has been achieved. Using Morse code enables the operator to use the hobby quietly without making a lot of noise in the house. It is also a therapeutic means of communications and can be quite relaxing.

Most amateurs that have taken the trouble to learn Morse can copy speeds of 30 WPM plus, in their heads. At that speed and ability it becomes conversation, with no need to write it down, other than jotting down notes on which to comment. At this stage it is pure pleasure. Although the traditional straight key is still used by many, at this speed it is not possible, and electronic keyers become essential pieces of equipment for the Morse enthusiast. Contests are operated by using computer software and keyboard control, with macros selected by the operator. (*see* Chapter 5).

Morse code has a 21st century role as an assistive technology, helping people with a variety of disabilities to communicate. Morse can be sent by someone with severe motion

## Advantages of using Morse code

1.   **Simple equipment.** It is possible to build a simple CW transmitter using fewer than a dozen parts, and a direct conversion receiver can give acceptable performance on CW. The art of 'homebrewing' is alive and well, and building a CW transmitter and/or receiver can get an amateur onto the air on CW very easily and cheaply.

2.   **International.** It is easy to get around the language barrier by the use of abbreviations such as *QTH* and *73*, so that two amateurs can have an elementary contact without knowing each other's language, and without accent or phonetic problems that may arise on phone.

3.   **Silent operation.** Wearing headphones and using a straight key or bug, it is possible to operate CW silently, at night time without disturbing others sleeping in the house. Similarly, holiday operation on CW from a hotel can be done in 'stealth' mode.

4.   **Morse gets through.** Cross-mode contacts aren't very common, perhaps because they're not valid for most awards, but when struggling to copy a weak phone station on a crowded band it's surprising how often a switch to CW will enable the contact to be completed.

5.   **Spectrum efficiency.** The minimum bandwidth needed to copy an SSB signal is about 1.8kHz, and to sound natural the requirement is more like 2.5kHz. On the other hand IF filters for CW operation are typically only 500Hz wide, and if necessary CW can be copied through filters of 100Hz or less. Put simply, at least five times as many CW contacts can fit in the bandwidth required for SSB.

6.   **Less breakthrough.** Those who operate both modes know that breakthrough problems are worse on SSB than CW. It is always better to try to resolve a TVI or RFI problem but if this is not possible it may be that switching to CW enables operation to continue when it is impossible on phone. And if power has to be reduced, CW comes into its own.

7.   **More competitive.** The difference between 'big gun' and 'little pistol' seems to be accentuated on phone. The low power or antenna-limited operator may struggle for contacts on phone, whereas CW is a great leveller.

8.   **Morse is a skill.** It's wrong to say that phone operation doesn't require skill, but the basic skill required is that of speech, which just about everyone has. On the other hand, a new skill has to be learned in order to be able to communicate using CW, and the sense of achievement can be considerable.

9.   **Automation.** There are computer programs which make it possible to automate the transmission and reception of Morse code. This makes it possible under some conditions to engage in CW contacts without knowing the code, but this would be to miss the whole point: it would be much better to use a more efficient automated mode such as PSK31. In any case, a good human operator can easily out-perform most computer techniques when copying a CW signal on a channel with even a moderate amount of interference or fading.

10.   **Morse is easy.** Most people think of Morse code as a language, and at special event stations Morse operation always proves fascinating to visitors. All that is needed to acquire Morse skills is to learn the symbols for 26 letters, ten numbers and a few special characters. This is a great deal easier than learning a foreign language complete with all its grammar and vocabulary.

disability, as long as they have some minimal motor control. In some cases this means alternately blowing into and sucking on a plastic tube ("puff and sip" interface). People with severe sensory disabilities (eg deaf and blind) can receive Morse through a skin buzzer. Products are available that allow a computer operating system to be controlled by Morse code, allowing the user access to the Internet and electronic mail.

In the early days of radio, it was difficult to construct equipment capable of sending and receiving signals using voice, and modulation methods then were quite expensive to employ, so Morse code was the only means available. Morse code remains the simplest and most efficient way known to send messages via radio. It is easier to construct a Morse code transmitter and receiver than any other communications apparatus, and messages can be sent with very low transmitted power. Morse code signals (also known as CW, (*Continuous Wave*)) penetrate interference, both natural and man-made, better than most of the more complex schemes.

It is entirely possible to construct a working Amateur Radio transmitter/receiver for only a few pounds, including antenna and accessories, and (using Morse code) use it to contact stations thousands of miles away. In fact, an entire group of Amateur Radio enthusiasts specialise in building and using very simple, low powered stations (known as QRP, in ham radio parlance). There are thousands of QRP (*low power*) enthusiasts around the world. The relative power efficiency of CW is of particular benefit to operators who use simple low-powered stations, which is likely to be the case for operators from developing nations. Using such home-made equipment provides more satisfaction than using a commercial one bought off a shelf.

# Chapter 3

# Learning the Code

Some people make the mistake of thinking that the first step to learning Morse is to go out and buy a Morse key. This is the wrong approach. This is where the bad news comes in! There is no short cut or easy ways of learning the code. It boils down to you, time and patience and a lot of hard work. There is an old saying that is quite appropriate here. "Winners never quit but quitters never win".

This is the point at which you decide whether to embark on this project or not. It is the point at which all the hard work ON YOUR PART begins. Nobody else can do it for you and it is not achievable in one weekend, a week or even a month.

First of all, the alphabet and numbers 0-9 have to be learned parrot fashion. I am a firm believer in learning the whole code at once. Some people advocate learning small groups of three or four letters, but I feel that learning the complete alphabet is the way to go. However, just adopt the method that suits you best. You are going to have to learn the whole character set anyway. The following characters are the basic minimum that should be learned, and these include punctuation and pro-signs.

You must remember that dots are dits, and dashes are dahs. Looking at the letter A, for example (**Fig 3.1**), you might think it is dot-dash. Again this is the wrong approach. It is, in fact, dit-dah, pronounced di-dah. The T remains silent. Learning all the characters in this fashion will give you a fundamental sound in your head. Carrying it on to the letter B, it would be dah-di-di-dit.

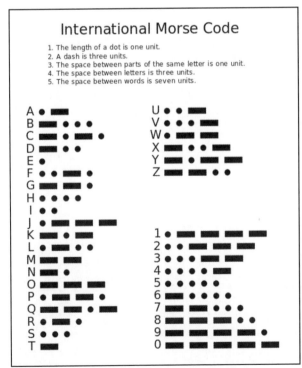

*Fig 3.1: Morse Characters as dots and dashes*

# Common Abbreviations

| | | | | | | |
|---|---|---|---|---|---|---|
| AA | All after | HW | How | SIG | Signature; |
| AB | All before | LID | A poor operator | | Signal |
| ABT | About | MA | Milliamperes | SINE | Operator's personal initials |
| ADR | Address | MILS | Milliamperes | SKED | Schedule |
| AGN | Again | MSG | Message; | SRI | Sorry |
| AM | Amplitude Modulation | | Prefix to radiogram | SSB | Single Side Band |
| ANT | Antenna | N | No | SVC | Service; |
| BCI | Broadcast Interference | NCS | Net Control Station | | Prefix to service message |
| BCL | Broadcast Listener | ND | Nothing Doing | T | Zero |
| BK | Break, Break in | NIL | Nothing; | TFC | Traffic |
| BN | All between; | | I have nothing for you | TMW | Tomorrow |
| | Been | NM | No more | TKS | Thanks |
| BUG | Semi-Automatic key | NR | Number | TNX | Thanks |
| B4 | Before | NW | Now; | TT | That |
| C | Yes | | I resume transmission | TU | Thank you |
| CFM | Confirm; | OB | Old boy | TVI | Television interference |
| | I confirm | OC | Old chap | TX | Transmitter |
| CK | Check | OM | Old man | TXT | Text |
| CL | I am closing my station; | OP | Operator | UR | Your; |
| | Call or nickname | OPR | Operator | | You're |
| CLD | Called | OT | Old timer; | URS | Yours |
| CLG | Calling | | Old top | VFO | Variable Frequency Oscillator |
| CQ | Calling any station | PBL | Preamble | VY | Very |
| CW | Continuous wave | PSE | Please | WA | Word after |
| DLD | Delivered | PWR | Power | WB | Word before |
| DLVD | Delivered | PX | Press | WD | Word |
| DR | Dear | R | Received as transmitted; | WDS | Words |
| DX | Distance | | Are | WKD | Worked |
| ES | And | RCD | Received | WKG | Working |
| FB | Fine Business, excellent | RCVR | Receiver | WL | Well; |
| FM | Frequency Modulation | RX | Receiver | | Will |
| GA | Go ahead | REF | Refer to; | WUD | Would |
| GM | Good morning | | Referring to; | WX | Weather |
| GN | Good night | | Reference | XCVR | Transceiver |
| GND | Ground | RFI | Radio frequency interference | XMTR | Transmitter |
| GUD | Good | RIG | Station equipment | XTAL | Crystal |
| HI | The telegraph laugh; | RTTY | Radio teletype | XYL | Wife |
| | High | SASE | Self-addressed, stamped | YL | Young lady |
| HR | Here; | | envelope | 73 | Best Regards |
| | Hear | SED | Said | 88 | Hugs and Kisses |
| HV | Have | | | | |

*Fig 3.2*: *Common abbreviations used on Morse code*

## Q Signals (they take the form of a question only when followed by a question mark)

| | | |
|---|---|---|
| QRG | Will you tell me my exact freq (or that of ___)? | Your exact frequency (or that of ___) is ___ kHz. |
| QRH | Does my frequency vary? | Your frequency varies. |
| QRI | How is the tone of my transmission? | The tone of your transmission is ___. |
| | | (1 Good, 2 Variable, 3. Bad) |
| QRJ | Are you receiving me badly? | I can not receive you. Your signals are too weak. |
| QRK | What is the intelligibility of my signals | The intelligibility of your signals (or those of ___) is: |
| | (or those of ___)? | (1 Bad, 2 Poor, 3 Fair, 4 Good, 5 Excellent) |
| QRL | Are you busy? | I am busy (or I am busy with ___). Please do not interfere. |
| QRM | Is my transmission being interfered with? | Your transmission is being interfered with ___. |
| | | (1 Nil, 2 Slightly, 3 Moderately, 4 Severely, 5 Extremely) |
| QRN | Are you troubled by static? | I am troubled by static ——. (1-5 as under QRM) |
| QRO | Shall I increase power? | Increase power. |
| QRP | Shall I decrease power? | Decrease power. |
| QRQ | Shall I send faster? | Send faster ___. (WPM) |
| QRS | Shall I send more slowly? | Send more slowly ___. (WPM) |
| QRT | Shall I stop sending? | Stop sending. |
| QRU | Have you anything for me? | I have nothing for you. |
| QRV | Are you ready? | I am ready. |
| QRW | Shall I inform ___ that you are calling on ___ kHz? | Please inform ___ that I am calling on ___ kHz. |
| QRX | When will you call me again? | I will call you again at ___ hours (on ___ kHz). |
| QRY | What is my turn? | Your turn is numbered ___. |
| QRZ | Who is calling me? | You are being called by ___ (on ___ kHz). |
| QSA | What is the strength of my signals | The strength of you signals (or those of ___) is ___. |
| | (or those of ___)? | (1 Scarcely perceptible, 2 Weak, 3 Fairly good, |
| | | 4 Good, 5 Very good) |
| QSB | Are my signals fading? | Your signals are fading. |
| QSD | Is my keying defective? | Your keying is defective? |
| QSG | Shall I send ___ messages at a time? | Send ___ messages at a time. |
| QSK | Can you hear me in between your signals and | I can hear you between my signals; |
| | if so, can I break in on your transmission? | break in on my transmission. |
| QSL | Can you acknowledge receipt? | I am acknowledging receipt. |
| QSM | Shall I repeat the last message I sent you, | Repeat the last message you sent me |
| | or some previous message? | [or message(s) number(s) ___]. |
| QSN | Did you hear e (or ___) on ___ kHz? | I did hear you (or ___) on ___ kHz. |
| QSO | Can you communicate with ___ direct or by relay? | I can communicate with ___ direct (or by relay through ___) |
| QSP | Will you relay to ___? | I will relay to ___. |
| QST | General call preceding a message addressed to all | |
| | amateurs & ARRL members. In effect "CQ ARRL". | |
| QSU | Shall I send or reply on this freq (or on ___ kHz)? | Send a series of Vs on this frequency (or on ___ kHz). |
| QSW | Will you send on this frequency (or on ___ kHz)? | I am going to send on this frequency (or on ___ kHz). |
| QSX | Will you listen to ___ on ___ kHz? | I am listening to ___ on ___ kHz. |
| QSY | Shall I change to to transmission on another freq? | Change transmission to another frequency (or ___ kHz). |
| QSZ | Shall I send each word or group more than once? | Send each word or group twice (or ___ times). |
| QTA | Shall I cancel message number ___? | Cancel message number ___. |
| QTB | Do you agree with my counting of words? | I do not agree with your counting of words. I will repeat |
| | | the first letter or digit of each word or group. |
| QTC | How many messages have you to send? | I have ___ messages for you (or for ___). |
| QTH | What is your location? | My location is ___. |
| QTR | What is the correct time? | The correct time is ___. |

**Fig 3.3**: *International Q-code definitions. Not all are in common use in amateur radio*

| R-S-T Number | Readability R | Strength S | Tone T (CW only) |
|---|---|---|---|
| 1 | Unreadable | Faint signals, barely perceptible | 60Hz or less, very rough and broad |
| 2 | Barely readable, occasional words distinguishable | Very weak signals | Very rough AC, very harsh and broad |
| 3 | Readable with considerable difficulty | Weak signals | Rough AC tone, rectified but not filtered |
| 4 | Readable with practically no difficulty | Fair signals | Rough note, some trace of filtering |
| 5 | Perfectly readable | Fairly good signals | Filtered rectified AC but strongly ripple-modulated |
| 6 | N/A | Good signals | Filtered tone, definite trace of ripple modulation |
| 7 | N/A | Moderately strong signals | Near pure tone, trace of ripple modulation |
| 8 | N/A | Strong signals | Near perfect tone, slight trace of modulation |
| 9 | N/A | Extremely strong signals | Perfect tone, no trace of ripple or modulation of any kind |

*Fig 3.4*: Signal Reports: Readability, Strength, and Tone. Note that a letter may be added to the RST numbers to report a chirped note ('C'), key clicks ('K') or a perfect tone as though the transmission was crystal controlled ('X') though this latter is rarely used these days

The last dit has the T on it this time. I am sure you can follow this, so take the whole alphabet in this fashion and try to get help from a family member. Get them to ask you letters and numbers at random, with you converting them to Morse in response until there is no thinking time at all.

- One dah is equal in length to 3 dits.
- The space between elements of a character is equal to 1 dit.
- The space between characters is equal to 3 dits.
- The space between words is equal to 7 dits.

The code in di-dah fashion is shown in Fig 3. Morse Characters in di-dah fashion and learning the code in this way makes it sound like Morse and will also make it easier for the student to repeat the code out loud.

Another good idea is to make a series of cards, roughly the size of the old cigarette cards. On one side is the letter or number and on the other the Morse, in 'di-dah' fashion. Have them in your pocket and when you have a spare minute or two, pull one out at random, and convert it, either way. You can also use the CD associated with this book and just listen to the Morse in your car as you drive. Conversion in that way will soon commit the code to memory.

There are other ways of conversion, too. For example, if you are driving, convert the number plate of the vehicle in front to Morse code. Do the same for advertisements, shop signs and so on.

You will also need a minimal amount of punctuation plus some commonly used pro-signs. There are only four commonly used punctuation marks, comma, full-stop, question-mark and slash-bar.

These all have to be retained in memory for instant recall.

## Prosigns and Other Procedural Signals for Morse Code

Prosigns are symbols formed by running together two characters into one without the intercharacter space, to make an abbreviation for the most common procedural signals. Usually written with a BAR over the characters. The ones in < > are considered by the ARRL as prosigns -- see ARRL page URL:

*http://www.arrl.org/FandES/field/nts-mpg/pdf/MPG304A.pdf*

| | |
|---|---|
| <AAA> | Full Stop |
| <KA> | Beginning of message |
| <VE> | Beginning of transmission (alternative to above) |
| <AR> | End of message |
| <AS> | Stand by; wait |
| <BT> | Separation (break) between address and text; between text and signature. |
| <HH> | (Error in sending. 8 dits - Transmission continues with last word correctly sent.) |
| <IMI> | Repeat; I say again. (Difficult or unusual words or groups.) |
| <NR> | Number follows |
| <SK> | End of work or close down (end of communications, no reply expected.) |

The following without the < > are other commonly used two letter procedural signals. These are usually sent as two separate letters.

| | |
|---|---|
| BK | Break |
| CL | Going off the air (clear) |
| CQ | Calling any amateur radio station (Many add a space between the C and the Q) |
| DE | This or From |
| KN | Go only, invite a specific station to transmit |

### Commonly used in CW - single letter meanings:

| | |
|---|---|
| C | Correct yes |
| K | Go, invite any station to transmit |
| N | No Negative |
| R | All received OK |

## Explanation of Prosigns and other procedural signals

Pro-signs are symbols formed by running together two or three characters into one, without the inter-character space, to make an abbreviation for the most common procedural signals. They are often written with a BAR over the characters as shown in **Fig 3.5.**

The ARRL lists the following prosigns on their document which can be found on the Internet at:
*http://www.arrl.org/FandES/field/nts-mpg/pdf/MPG304A.pdf*

## Prosigns and Other Procedural Signals

The following are usually sent by running the characters together into one, without the inter-character space (indicated by the brackets, which are not sent).

| | |
|---|---|
| <AAA> | Full Stop |
| <KA> | Beginning of message |
| <VE> | Beginning of transmission (alternative to above) |
| <AR> | End of message |
| <AS> | Stand by; wait |
| <BT> | Separation (break) between address & text; between text & signature |
| <HH> | (Error in sending. 8 dits - Transmission continues with last word correctly sent.) |
| <IMI> | Repeat; I say again. (Difficult or unusual words or groups.) |
| <NR> | Number follows |
| <SK> | End of work or close down (end of communications, no reply expected.) |

The following without the < > are other commonly used two letter procedural signals.

These are usually sent as two separate letters.

| | |
|---|---|
| BK | Break |
| CL | Going off the air (clear) |
| CQ | Calling any station (Many add a space between the C and the Q) |
| DE | This or From |
| KN | Go only, invite a specific station to transmit |

The following single letter codes are commonly used in CW

| | |
|---|---|
| C | Correct, yes |
| K | Go, invite any station to transmit |
| N | No, negative |
| R | All received OK |

*Fig 3.5: Procedural signals enable Morse messages to be shortened and to cross language barriers*

## Prosign Tips

Don't neglect to learn these by sound. Knowing what they look like on paper is of little value when you are mystified by the sound of long CW characters. Knowing the rules of context that govern the use of prosigns is also very helpful. It will give you the knowledge of when and how to use them.

**AAA** is the period. Use it at the end of a sentence when the following sentence will pertain to the same subject.

**AR** is used at the end of a transmission when calling a specific station before the two-way contact has been established. It is usually followed by a K or KN when answering a

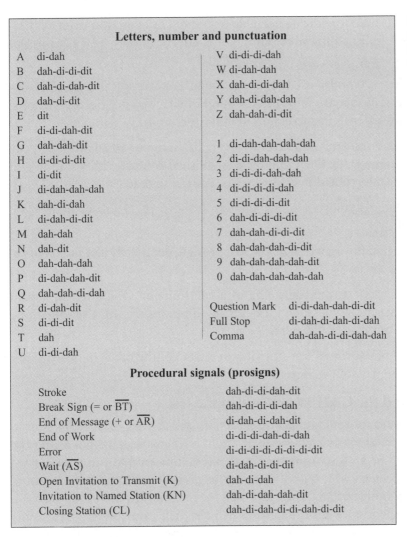

**Letters, number and punctuation**

| | | | | |
|---|---|---|---|---|
| A | di-dah | | V | di-di-di-dah |
| B | dah-di-di-dit | | W | di-dah-dah |
| C | dah-di-dah-dit | | X | dah-di-di-dah |
| D | dah-di-dit | | Y | dah-di-dah-dah |
| E | dit | | Z | dah-dah-di-dit |
| F | di-di-dah-dit | | | |
| G | dah-dah-dit | | 1 | di-dah-dah-dah-dah |
| H | di-di-di-dit | | 2 | di-di-dah-dah-dah |
| I | di-dit | | 3 | di-di-di-dah-dah |
| J | di-dah-dah-dah | | 4 | di-di-di-di-dah |
| K | dah-di-dah | | 5 | di-di-di-di-dit |
| L | di-dah-di-dit | | 6 | dah-di-di-di-dit |
| M | dah-dah | | 7 | dah-dah-di-di-dit |
| N | dah-dit | | 8 | dah-dah-dah-di-dit |
| O | dah-dah-dah | | 9 | dah-dah-dah-dah-dit |
| P | di-dah-dah-dit | | 0 | dah-dah-dah-dah-dah |
| Q | dah-dah-di-dah | | | |
| R | di-dah-dit | | Question Mark | di-di-dah-dah-di-dit |
| S | di-di-dit | | Full Stop | di-dah-di-dah-di-dah |
| T | dah | | Comma | dah-dah-di-di-dah-dah |
| U | di-di-dah | | | |

**Procedural signals (prosigns)**

| | |
|---|---|
| Stroke | dah-di-di-dah-dit |
| Break Sign (= or $\overline{BT}$) | dah-di-di-di-dah |
| End of Message (+ or $\overline{AR}$) | di-dah-di-dah-dit |
| End of Work | di-di-di-dah-di-dah |
| Error | di-di-di-di-di-di-dit |
| Wait ($\overline{AS}$) | di-dah-di-di-dit |
| Open Invitation to Transmit (K) | dah-di-dah |
| Invitation to Named Station (KN) | dah-di-dah-dah-dit |
| Closing Station (CL) | dah-di-dah-di-di-dah-di-dit |

*Fig 3.6: Morse code displayed as it sounds - the best way to remeber it*

CQ, or calling someone for a sked.

**AS** means "Please stand by for a moment", usually used to let the other guy know that you have to talk to someone else in the room, answer the telephone, or fix some technicial glitch and that you have not just switched off or had a transmitter fault. You'll be back in just a minute.

**BT** is like thinking pause. Use it at the end of a sentence when the next sentence will pertain to a different topic, or when you are thinking of what to send next.

**CL** follows **SK** when you are also vacating the frequency just used. Note that the letters are not run together on this one. It's barred but normally sent as two distinct letters and means you will not answer any other calls.

**DE** From

**DN** is the slash (/). It is used to indicate portable operation, or operation from a different call area than that indicated by your callsign. It is not commonly seen as a prosign but as a punctuation mark.

**IMI** is the question mark. It is also used for a repeat sign. For example: Name hr is Roger ? Roger, with the question mark indicating a repeat of what has just been sent. Some operators also use two letter I's in succession to indicate a repeat.

**K** is used at the end of a transmission means you are listening for an answer from any station. Use it when calling CQ. Once you have established contact with a station and you do not want to be interrupted by a third party, use KN instead.

**KN** is used at at the end of a transmission when only the other party already in the QSO is invited to respond.

**MIM** is the comma, again not seen designated as a prosign, but merely as a punctuation mark.

**R** means "Received". Use it at the beginning of a transmission ONLY if you copied 100% of what was just sent to you. Don't use it if anything was missed. Use something like "FB on UR QTH but missed UR name".

**SK** is used at the end of your final transmission of a QSO. If the other station has not yet sent his "final" you may follow SK with KN.

## Tuition Groups and the GB2CW Scheme in the UK

One suggestion I would thoroughly recommend is to ask at your local radio club to find if there is an active Morse tuition group. It might be that your Club has a GB2CW volunteer. This would be an RSGB member who has volunteered to run a session on the air, normally two metre FM, once a week for beginners and improvers. It would be well worthwhile joining such a group, not only for the one-to-one tuition that you will receive, but competition within the group will also help your progress. Not only that, it is a lot of fun too, and it relieves any stress that some might have. I have taught Morse for a number of years now and I find that group learning is the best way to get the best from each member of the group. A light-hearted approach also helps, whilst maintaining steady progress. Normally it takes about 12 weeks to reach 12WPM with one meeting per week and roughly 30-60 minutes practice per day.

Having said a light-hearted approach is fine, progress is dependent absolutely on the amount of practice put in, and the group tutor will be able to tell if any has been done, so dedication is mandatory. It is much like learning the piano: performance is directly proportional to the amount of practice you are prepared to put in.

There are also a number of dedicated Clubs that you can join. This usually entails contact on the air however, so this approach is best undertaken when a suitable level of skill in sending has been attained.

## The Candler System

By1904 Walter H. Candler had learned the American Morse code and worked for two years as a telegrapher. He had practiced diligently and felt qualified to apply for a job as commercial relay operator in the Western Union office at Atlanta GA. But he didn't last out there even one day, and had to take a night shift job as telegraph operator at a small town R.R. station. He was deeply hurt and puzzled. What was the matter? What mysterious ingredient was missing?

It was then that he began to realise that telegraphy is primarily a mental process, and that the so-called "sub-conscious mind" must play a vital part in it. (At that time here was quite a bit of popular writing about the "sub-conscious mind," which no doubt helped him put it all together.) He began experimenting until he had solved his own problem and mastered the code himself, and in time he became qualified to teach others how to do it, too. By 1911 he had established his own "school" in Chicago to teach "The Candler System," later moving it to Asheville, NC.

Develop "SOUND CONSCIOUSNESS." -- In Lesson 7 he wrote: "In learning code it is necessary to consciously count the dits and dahs of the various signals, both in sending and receiving. By repetition, the sub-conscious mind gradually assumes this burden of counting them. As long as you must consciously count them, work will be slow, but as the sub-mind takes them, they go faster and faster." "As you progress," he wrote elsewhere, "Begin to respond more readily to the sound patterns than to visual ones: learn to shift from what you mentally see to what you hear. So long as you must consciously remind yourself that so many dits and dahs 'stand' for certain letters, you are not learning code." So, "when you hear didah, no longer say to yourself: 'didah stands for A.' Instead, when you hear didah, hear A. Do not translate." "In learning code you do not have to relearn words, but you do have to change the approach...from visual to auditory... Once you have mastered this consciously, your sub-mind will handle that detail, and do a faster, better job than your conscious mind possibly can."

It certainly has a very good point and could be very useful to try to learn Morse like this from the start. They do eventually make certain patterns in your mind and so will words themselves and once proficient, you won't

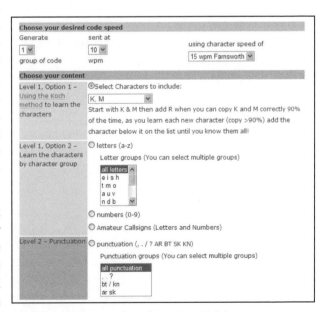

Fig 3.7: Part of a screen from the AA9PW Training program

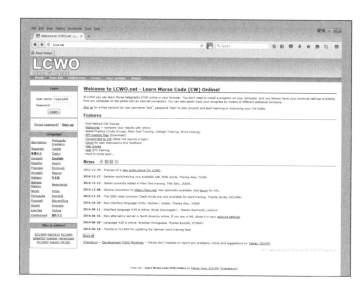

*Fig 3.8: Part of the Learn CW Online training page*

even know you are translating Morse because it will sound just like conversation. That is when it becomes pure enjoyment!

## Using your Computer

There are several learning programs available as freeware that can assist in several different ways. Links to these, or in some cases the software itself, can be found on the CD provided free with this book.

The excellent AA9PW Morse Practice Program (**Fig 3.7**) is available on the Internet at: *http://www.aa9pw.com/radio/morse.html and is an interactive program.*

You don't have to download anything, just work from the page that appears on your screen.

I use this program in my Morse tuition classes and find it invaluable. The page you will see when you use the above URL will generate morse code consisting of groups of random characters and there are 25 characters per group (five sets of five characters).You can pick which group of characters you wish to be test-ed on: the alphabet, the numbers or punctuation (including prosigns) or all three. The computer creates an audio file and sends that to your browser so your browser (or helper application) needs to be capable of handling these files. You will also need a sound card with speakers or similar to be able to hear the Morse. There are several levels, starting with letters and numbers which is the obvious one to start with. You can start as low as 5WPM and increase up to 50WPM if you feel brave enough! The audio files on the CD attached to this book were made using AA9PW's page.

Learn CW on-line is very useful. Here you can be trained on the keyboard as well, so that will improve your typing skill. You can also download a file of common words, starting with 100 or so, and with Learn CW on-line ( LCWOL ) you can turn these into MP3 files, save them onto a portable MP3 player and take them with you, in the car or out walking the dog.  But learning Morse this way accustoms the student to the sound of words, and that is when your speed will increase.

There are many other programs you can use for basic training of course and if you want a varied selection just search for Morse programs on the Internet (or use the links on the CD) and you will find dozens of them.

Always select a speed just above that which you can receive fully. Once you achieve that level, increase the speed again. In this way, you are striving to achieve complete copy all the time. It is the only way to improve. Once you feel comfortable at around nine words per minute with the letters and numbers, try the punctuation. This will seem easier as there are only four that you really need bother about. When you are happy with those, try some call signs.

Mixed letters and numbers always slow you down again, but you should persevere here because obviously call signs are going to be a large part of your use of Morse code on the amateur bands. However, when selecting the speed, use a character speed of 15WPM Farnsworth timing. The Morse will then be sent to you at 15WPM for each character with a large space enabling thinking time. If you start at something like 5WPM, the character speed is too laborious and using the Farnsworth method is by far the best way of learning. This is discussed in Chapter 4.

Don't forget that the learning process takes time and is proportional to the time that you devote to it. There is nothing magic in this process, just a lot of hard work.

## A summary of learning processes

**Audible** - Probably the most popular and effective method. For many, the instant recognition of a SOUND and the association with a character (letter, number, punctuation, prosign) or whole word is usually recommended. The less interpretation needed between the initial hearing and recognition, the better. As you progress - try not to repeat the sound -- just strive for instant recognition.

**Musically Or Language Associated** -- Some learn musically or language associated- some learn it as a song or word --

> dah dah ditit -- The zebra did it - letter Z.
> dah dah di dah here comes the bride - she is a queen - letter Q.
> Dog did it," "dah-di-di!" Letter D - *See* Code Quick

One musician recommends: "As for the music and CW, it may appeal to you. It's the rhythm that does it. Tap your foot to a 4 x 1 cadence. Then tap your finger on the desk in sequence with it. Tap it three times and you have a "S" tap it four times you have a "H" tap it five times you have a "5". Now do this while keeping the foot going: Send a "V" di di dit dah. Keep in cadence. Catch the rhythm? Think of Beethoven's 5th symphony!

**Audible Phonetics** - Some learn by associating it with the NATO Alphabet i.e, dit-dah followed by A or ALPHA after a while you will hear dit dah and A or alpha pops into the brain.

**Patterns** -There are patterns in Morse code letters. For example: the letter A is similar to the letter W except that the letter W has an additional dah to it. One might study A (didah), W (didadah), J (didahdahdah), 1(didahdahdahdah) in order, then mixed. This is effective if one has difficulty in discerning J from 1 etc.

**Typing** - some find that they have an automatic reflex to hearing a character and hitting the right key on a keyboard. This would also provide practice for your typing skill as well as co-ordination skill. Visually impaired people can also use a Braille keyboard for the blind.

**Characters** - It is best to have the characters sent at 12 wpm with 5 wpm spacing. Below this speed, the mind perceives the sound of the individual elements, and not the sound of the whole element.

**Plain Text Vs Mixed Random Characters** Studying Morse in plain text gives the advantage of being able to anticipate what is coming next where mixed random characters – you must know them all. Maybe practice both if that works for you.

**Koch Method** - Learn Morse code using high speed random characters.

Farnsworth - Farnsworth Morse is composed of higher speed characters sent with longer than standard spacing between them. This means that the mind gets used to hearing the "right sounds" while having plenty of time to think about them. All the great code schools of the past used Farnsworth teaching.

**Brain Soak** – Try and just listen to code practice text with the text in front of you as you listen to the Morse. This works for some until one day it just all comes together. The impediment to increasing speed and proficiency is called a barrier which you may feel you will never hurdle, but is amazing when one day after brain soaking – it magically all comes together. Your mileage may vary.

**Computer Programs And Courses** - There are many available – Look for Morse Programs on the internet and try them out -- choose the one that works the best for you. Remember that the one that works for your friend or elmer may or may not be the best for you.

For Many - studying EVERY day for 15 to 30 minutes is successful. Leaving long periods between study sessions is usually counter-productive. Studying for long periods at a session - frazzles many a brain.

Whatever method you use, try to 'hear' the code directly as a letter. In other words, don't try to translate the sound into dot-dash and translate that into A, just hear the dot-dash and think A. Easier said than done, but when you master it your receiving speed will increase dramatically.

Finally - there is no one guaranteed method -- the learner is encouraged to try the methods and programs that give the best results.

Also Excellent Reading "The Art & Skill of Radio Telegraphy" By William G. Pierpont N0HFF -- Available for downloading in PDF

# Chapter 4

# Progressing to 12-15WPM

By now you should have learned the complete alphabet, the ten numerals and also the four punctuation marks at the very minimum. If you have also committed to memory the prosigns, and also started learning the abbreviations, then bravo! It proves that you are enthusiastic enough to devote a regular time-table of practice per day to the task.

So, here is a review of some of the various methods of practice that you can adopt. Try them all, each has their advantages and you will find a method that you will prefer on a personal basis and one that shows more improvement than others.

Some methods of learning basics are bad enough to be completely avoided, such as learning opposites, or visualising Morse code as heaped numbers of dots and dashes, or worse still, sending it on a key. Please *do NOT touch* a Morse key until you can receive at around 12-15WPM and then only under supervision of an experienced operator.

## Morse Code Speed

To understand code speed, it is helpful to look at the method in which code is generated. Morse code dits (dots) and dahs (dashes) and the spaces between them are sent using standard fixed time intervals. A dit takes one unit of time, a dah takes three units of time, the space between dits and dahs of the same character takes one unit of time, the space between characters takes three units of time, and the space between words takes seven units of time. See the table below and the diagram. When sending Morse at a given speed, these units of time remain fixed in duration, and consequently the letters and words take varying amounts of time to send. For example, an `E' (dit) takes one unit of time to send while a `Y' (dah-di-dah-dah) takes 13 units of time to send. Similarly, words, even those having the standard number of characters (five), will take varying amounts of time to send.

Code speed is given as a number of words per minute (WPM). Because characters take different amounts of time to send, and because words have different numbers of characters (although we use 5 letters as the average word size), code speed must be based on the sending of a standard "word". PARIS is commonly used as this standard word.

PARIS, which takes 50 units of time to send (including the space between words), is representative of Standard English text; i.e., it takes about the same amount of time to send as the average word. Morse code was purposefully designed so that the more common characters, such as `E' and `T', take the shortest amount of time to send, making the average text flow as quickly as possible.

## Standard timing

Standard timing is as follows: *(and shown graphically in* **Fig 4.1***)*

> The period of a single dot is one unit, measured in seconds.
> A dash is a period of three units.
> A period of one unit separates each element (dot or dash) within a character.
> A period of three units separates each character within a word.
> A period of seven units separates each word.

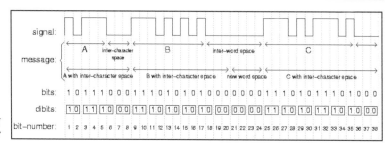

*Fig 4.1: Morse timing shown graphically*

## The Farnsworth method

From teaching the code for years and having quite a good success rate, I prefer using the Farnsworth method. The Farnsworth timing came from the late Donald R "Russ" Farnsworth, W6TTB, who in the late 1950s asked Bart Bartlett, W6OWP, to help him prepare some tapes for a code course he had developed. Farnsworth's unique method of instruction was to maintain the code speed for individual characters but allowing longer spaces.

Farnsworth timing is defined as sending the characters at a faster speed than the words. For example, sending the characters at 20WPM but adding enough time between them to slow down the overall rate to 10WPM gives a certain amount of thinking time. The idea is that you are listening to Morse characters at a speed that you will eventually be using and that pattern should be instilled in your mind.

Once you reach 20WPM, the spacing is correct for that speed and you can then progress further either by again increasing the character speed or leaving the spacing correct for the speed, thereby allowing true timing. Having reached 20WPM, it is experience and use of the mode that will improve your speed.

Eventually, as your proficiency increases, the gaps are closed up and the true speed is attained.

The problem in learning Morse is that at speeds above a few WPM, Morse is most easily read by ear when the characters are recognized rhythmically rather than by remembering the dots and dashes. But the person just learning Morse starts at very slow speeds, where thinking about the actual dots and dashes is easier than recognizing the slow rhythm of the characters. So in order to increase their ability to read Morse above a few words per minute, students are forced to shift from the "thinking of dots and dashes" mode to the rhythm recognition mode. Along the way,

*Fig 4.2*: *Morse Characters as dots and dashes*

there will be barriers which at the time seem insurmountable. This is the reason why many just give up. Donating a few minutes per week is not going to crack it! Dedication is needed, and I mean dedication. I usually quote the plate of bacon and eggs. The chicken "donated" to the breakfast plate, but the pig was dedicated! **Fig 4.2**

The idea behind the Farnsworth method is to eliminate the counting phase by sending the characters at a speed at which rhythm recognition is easy and counting is not. This forces the student to learn the rhythms. Initially, the rate of transmission is slowed (by the addition of time (between characters) to allow the student to gradually build the skill at recognising and writing the received text. The process by which the student recognizes the characters is never changed; he just gets better (faster) at doing so.

The ARRL has converted all of its Morse material to Farnsworth timing. They are using a standard of sending transmission at an 18-WPM character rate, but of course, at 18WPM and faster speeds, the ARRL transmission reverts to standard timing, since no extra time has to be inserted. This standard applies to all code practice and test tapes, and to W1AW transmissions.

## Morse Training by the Koch Method

Koch's method is a simple, direct way of building reflexes. However, it requires either a computer and Morse software or a personal trainer. That's why it was overlooked for so many years. Now that computers are commonplace, it could become the standard Morse training method. Here's how it works:

You start out by setting up your computer to send you Morse characters at 20 wpm and at an overall sending speed of at least 15 wpm. You then get out your paper and pencil and have the machine start sending -- but only two characters. That's right, for your first sessions, you'll only have two choices. Copy on paper for five minutes, then stop the machine and compare what you copied with what the machine sent. Count characters and calculate your percentage of correct copy.

If your score is 90 percent or better -- congratulations! You just learned your first two characters, and, importantly, you learned them at full speed. You'll never have to learn them over again. If you didn't make 90 percent, practice some more. As soon as you can copy the first two characters with 90 percent accuracy, add a third character to your practice. Your accuracy will drop as you work on assimilating the new character, but it will rise again to 90 percent or better. Then you add the fourth character, and so on.

This method does not allow you to build that lookup table in your brain. To copy at full speed, you MUST build the reflexes in order to achieve 90 percent accuracy. And that's what you're spending your time doing -- building reflexes. Think of it as a parallel to perfecting a tennis stroke or mastering a gymnastic routine; you're practicing until you get it right. The Koch method of building code proficiency character-by-character is similar to standard methods of teaching touch typing, another skill that must be reflexive.

This is a very individual method of training -- you progress at your own best speed, and spend only the time required to gain each new character. This means that you will waste no time in reaching your goal.

How much time is required? That will depend on the individual. You can get an idea of how long it's going to take after you've mastered a few characters. Keep track of your training sessions (some software will do this for you) and calculate your hours-per-character rate (or characters-per-hour if you're really fast!). That, multiplied by the amount of characters will give a rough idea of how long it's going to take.

While the Koch method is the fastest method of Morse training, speed alone is not its principal advantage. Its principal advantage, and a major difference from other methods, is that it provides you with constant positive reinforcement. This begins with your realization, after mastering the first two characters, that you CAN copy code at 15 or 20 wpm, because you just did it. After that, each new character mastered is further proof of your progress. Contrast that to slowly trying to build speed up from 4 or 5 wpm, then hitting the plateau at 10 wpm and seeing no progress for a long time. With the Koch method, frustration is at a minimum.

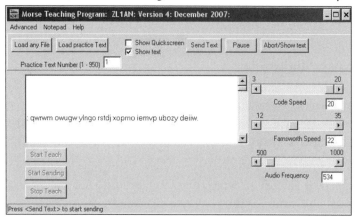

*Fig 4.3: Screen showing ZL1AN program after downloading*

Constant testing is necessary to ensure that you maximize the effectiveness of the Koch method. You must copy on paper, so you can grade yourself. Remember, if you score 90% accuracy or better, add another character. If you score any less than that, try again. By constantly testing yourself on continuous copying for at least five minutes, you know exactly how you're doing and exactly when you should add another character. This results in the fastest progress possible. The only problem with using this method in a class is that it is difficult to maintain everybody at the same level. Also, adding one character at a time can take much longer to master the complete character set necessary. This is why I prefer teaching the Farnsworth method, making the student learn the whole alphabet and numbers and then sending Morse to them to judge progress. The Koch method is very useful for practicing the awkward letters however, so a mix of both methods is probably a good idea. A Koch trainer can be downloaded from *http://www.g4fon.net/*.

## The Candler Method

Whilst this method dates back to the year dot, forgive the pun, it still has some advantages. I referred to this method in Chapter 2 and there is a complete description of it on the CD, but basically it is listening for sound patterns rather than learning dots and dashes right from the start. I have not had anybody who has used this system, but if it works for you then by all means use it. All the methods I have so far described are used in both learning the Code and then practicing to increase your speed.

## GB2CW in the UK

I am writing this paragraph as the RSGB GB2CW coordinator so obviously I am biased here! When I was first licensed, in 1956, Morse was mandatory and therefore anybody who wanted to become an amateur had to pass a GPO Morse test of 12WPM. This has now been discontinued. However, there is still a huge interest in the mode and it seems to be more popular now than ever with some newcomers to the hobby.

I was asked to rejuvenate a scheme that existed many years ago. Broadcasting is not allowed under the amateur licence as you know, but with the use of the special licence, GB2CW, it is possible to broadcast to a group of amateurs involved in learning Morse over the air.

Volunteer instructors are used in this way, and although there is a good pool of volunteers, there is never really enough and some areas don't have such a scheme active in their local Club. I would like to see ALL the UK Clubs have at least one GB2CW volunteer. There are few obstacles in the way and there is a great deal of satisfaction to be had from running a group. We have three volunteers in the Norwich Club, all taking different evenings and levels.

The qualifications needed are simple.
1 The ability to send and receive Morse at whatever speed you are teaching.
2 Membership of the RSGB necessary.
3 One hour per week to take the Class.
4 Good local coverage on two metres.
5 Obviously a two metre FM transceiver, and a computer.

If your Club does not have such a volunteer, then push for it and try to persuade some-body to take on the challenge. It really is good fun and great to see the progress of the students. There is a Morse Proficiency Certificate to be had at various speeds and it is a very worthy thing to do.

Take a look at the RSGB Web site:
*http://www.rsgb.org/operating/morse/*

Experience has shown that using two metres is by far the best method. The feedback is certain, there is little or no QRM, and using the local repeater extends the range for the class too, if simplex is not good enough. Using the repeater IS allowed, providing suitable pauses are given for mobiles etc.

## Use your computer

Mention has already been made of the AA9PW computer program for learning Morse in Chapter 3. It is a good idea to have a change too. A different sounding note, differ-ent content and style, some plain language perhaps; in that case try the ZL1AN Morse Code Teaching Program, the current version Teach 4 can be found on the CD provided with this book.

A screen shot is shown in (**Fig 3.7**) on page 23. This is the program that is used for teaching in Norfolk, UK. It is extremely versatile, and comes already loaded with around 1000 text files. However, the beauty of it is the fact that the tutor can construct his own files, whether it be plain language, numbers, letters, mixed groups and so on. Just construct a file in Notepad and import it into the root of Teach4. The new ver-sion also has a higher speed section, and the ability to change font. This is particularly useful when teaching for read-back. The ability to construct practice files makes this program my choice for tutoring. The note is a T9 note too which makes it very pleasant to listen to. A colon is used as a starting signal to prepare the students for copying. For plain language files I download news items from the NASA web site. These invariably contain proper names, and some of those can be Russian! There are also lots of refer-ences using a mixture of letters and numbers

You don't even have to load a program onto your computer. Go to:
*http://lcwo.net/about*

Learn CW Online is a site where you can do all sorts of things. You don't need to install a program on your computer, and you always have your personal settings available, from any computer on the globe with an internet connection. You can also easily track your progress by means of different statistical functions.

The site uses the Koch method and there are loads of training exercises, such as Code groups, Plain text, call sign training and word training. You can also download some MP3 practice files and take part in Highscores, comparing your results to others. Com-petition can provide a good stimulus to practice and improvement

As I have already suggested, it might be a good idea to record some MP3 files of your own and use them when in the car for example.

## Morse Boot Camps

It is a good idea to set up a Boot Camp to run various classes within your club. One would be for those with a basic knowledge of the code where the use of letter blocks, figure blocks, punctuation and the use of some plain language. The course helps to bolster their confidence when taking part in the GB2CW classes on the air. The second class is for intermediate students. This covers those from about 10 wpm up to about 15 wpm. The third would be for the more advanced students up to around 25 wpm. This works well at our local on-air classes. We have three of those each week on two metres, with a similar structure.

We also get some of the students to have supervised QSOs on the air from the station of G3LDI, where the course is run. That provides some encouragement for the student to make contacts from their own stations. It really is quite surprising how nervous some are about making their first QSO. Doing it this way with background help again provides the necessary encouragement for them to get on the air from their own stations.

*Fig 4.4*: *Shows Malcolm G3PDH around the table of torture! L/R is Jim G3YLA, Chris G4CCX, Malcolm G3PDH, Marshall M6DXL, Tony G0OOR and Paul G3SEM.*

Tea breaks and cake are also necessary and lots of discussion whilst having a break is a good way of sorting problems. I would encourage other clubs to put on a Boot camp. It really is a lot of fun! **Fig 4.4** shows Malcolm G3PDH around the table of torture!

Once a speed of around 15WPM has been attained, don't leave it there, carry on with the regular practice and set yourself targets: 20, 25, 30WPM, and so on. Code proficiency certificates are still available (**Fig 4.5**), but remember, to obtain these it will be necessary to write down what you are copying. This is not easy once you get over 25WPM unless regular practice is maintained. As you attain a higher speed, listening becomes more of a pleasure and not a chore, so try to improve all the time. Also, remember that Morse is an art form, as well as a skill. Take a pride in your ability at both receiving and sending as near perfect Morse as possible. If you send good

*Fig 4.5*: *Morse Proficiency Certificate*

Morse, you will never be short of a contact. It is so much easier to read well sent Morse and a pleasure to listen to.

## The Beauty of Morse

For someone with no knowledge of Morse Code at all, tuning across an amateur band, say 20 meters, on the CW end, and it will sound like a lot of noise, heterodynes, and QRM. For someone with ability to use Morse at around 25-30 wpm, tuning across the same band can produce a world of its own. With a pair of headphones on, a lively band, and a little time, the skilled operator can find new countries, listen to conversations, find the ARRL W1AW News broadcast, find old friends and stop for a chat, or if there happens to be a contest running, he can hone his operating skills even further. Some of the Russian CW operators use high-speed Morse, and speeds of 40-50wpm are not uncommon. Conversely, you can also find a lot of amateurs using speeds of 12-15WPM, having just got on the air. By working amateurs at the lower speeds, you should gain more confidence. Your speed will gradually increase the more time that you spend using Morse.

—•—•  ••••  •—  •——•  —  •  •—•        •••••

# Chapter 5

# Keys and Sending

By this time, you hopefully will have been dedicated enough with your practice and have now mastered around 12 to 15 words per minute fairly comfortably. Morse is now beginning to feel like an exciting mode, and you copy without really thinking about the translation from dots and dashes to letters and numbers. At this stage, it begins to be an automatic translation within the brain and also like another language, albeit somewhat slow. However, the character formation is embedded in your brain too, hopefully with the correct mark to space ratio and spacing, so now is a good time to turn to sending. Don't neglect the receiving practice though, because you really need to get to 25 words per minute for it to become really automatic. Then you will find yourself spending more time on the CW end of the bands.

## Using a Morse key under instruction

Some people think it is a waste of time learning to send on a straight key in this modern age of electronic keyers. The arguments against using a straight key vary, but these are a few. It's old fashioned and slow. Nobody uses straight keys any more. Morse sounds horrible when sent on a straight key. Most transceivers now have an electronic keyer built in so there is no need for a straight key. Why bother when we are going to end up using a paddle anyway.

Most of these arguments have a ring of truth to them, but I still feel it is necessary to be able to use a straight key properly. It is a skill that will remain with you for the rest of your life and you can derive a lot of pleasure from using a straight key on the air. Using a straight key also makes you form the characters using the proper mark/space ratio and forms the basis of sending good Morse eventually with a paddle.

Take advice from your instructor when buying a straight key. There are many variations available, some very poor, others mediocre, and some very good. It should be roughly 100mm by 180mm and weigh around 600 to 900 grams. It should be on a heavy base and made from brass, with a good centre pivot. It must have a space adjustment and good clean keying contacts, preferably silver plated. On some keys it is possible to adjust the tension as well. It should also have a standard doorknob, or mushroom with skirt, type knob, to allow proper holding of the key.

Prices vary, and will not be cheap for a good quality key. However, bear in mind that a straight key will last a lifetime and will always have a place in the shack of a true amateur. You can pay anything from around £60 up to a huge £600 for a really super-duper chrome plated key on a hand-polished serpentine base. There are regular contests called SKN's, Straight Key Night, in which it is not allowed to key with anything other than a straight key, and they can be a lot of fun. The key I have had for

*Fig 5.1: The authors straight key bought decades ago and is still going strong*

decades is still going strong and is shown in the picture in **Fig 5.1**. I have also been fortunate enough to find another very nice one called The Swedish Key, **Fig 5.2** a more modern key, and a pleasure to use. **Fig 5.2**a shows another Straight key, somewhat cheaper. It is the Czech straight key. This is a very solid key with a good action. However, it could use a heavier base and a doorknob type knob, instead of the flat one provided.

## Sending on a Straight Key

It is quite amusing to see how the whole Morse procedure is abused in some films. I have even seen a Morse key keyed with just the index finger, not that any real Morse was being sent!

**Fig 5.3** demonstrates the correct way to hold a Morse key. The first thing to do is to sit square to the table, with the key in line with your keying arm. I say this, because you may be left handed and prefer to key with the left hand rather than the right. Have the Morse key toward the front of the table, so that it is not possible to rest your arm on the table. The Americans teach sending on a straight key *with* the forearm resting on the table, but

*Fig 5.2a: Swedish Key*

*Fig 5.2b: Czech Key*

I think this leads to sloppy Morse. Hold the key with the index finger on the knob, and the thumb and middle finger on the skirt, as shown in the picture in **Fig 5.3**

I would prefer your instructor to show you how to key properly, as it does take some practice to get

*Fig 5.3: How to hold the Morse Key*

it correct. If you hold the key as shown in the picture, you should then key from the wrist. I call it the "limp wrist" method, using the arm as a lever, with the wrist being the actual point at which you form the Morse characters. Holding the key will then make the key follow your wrist. It is not easy to explain, but must be carried out correctly, hence my emphasis on an instructor. Bad habits are extremely difficult to break, and lead to bad Morse, which will inevitably lead to zero QSO's! You should be prepared to spend a lot of time perfecting this skill, especially if you want to be a good CW operator. Practising the rudiments will pay dividends in the long run, just like practicing scales on the piano for hours on end.

## Practice makes perfect – Morse

Your first sending session will preferably be with your instructor making sure that all is well with your technique. You will need to have a Morse practice oscillator. You can make one fairly easily on a piece of veroboard, using a 555 timer chip.

A suitable circuit is shown in **Fig 5.4** This takes a while to master in itself, but will bode well for the future, so time spent in doing it properly is time well spent. A lot of keyers can also be used for sending practice and even some modern transceivers have facilities for off air sending practice. Practice at home as you did with the reception, around 20 minutes a night minimum and try to emulate what you hear in the Morse program. A few weeks of this, gradually increasing the speed will ensure that your Morse will be as perfect as you can make it, providing you actually do the practice.

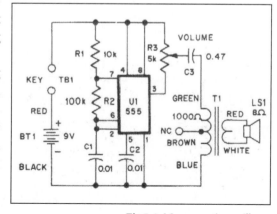

*Fig 5.4: Morse practice oscillator*

Once your instructor is happy with your results at around 18wpm, receiving and sending on the straight key, then it is time to think about a paddle.

## QSO Mode

Before discussing paddles, it might be a good idea to see the format of a basic Morse contact as it might happen on the air. There are many ways of making a contact (or 'QSO'), the standard rubber stamp short QSO (used mainly with those that have little command of the English language), contest QSO, DX style, and 'rag-chew'. The latter, if both stations let it, can carry on for an hour or more, depending on what you have to say to each other. Here are some examples:

### Example 1:

CQ CQ CQ de G9XXX G9XXX G9XXX AR PSE K

**G9XXX de G9YYY G9YYY AR KN**

G9YYY DE G9XXX GM = TU fer call = Name Chris QTH Norwich = UR RST 599 = Hw?
G9YYY de G9XXX AR KN

**G9XXX DE G9YYY TU Chris GM = UR RST 599 = Name Bernie**
**QTH LONDON = Nice meet u fer 1st time = Ant 3 el Yagi up 30 m = Pwr 100W = Wx hr fb**
**temp 30 C = G9XXX de G9YYY**
**AR KN**

G9YYY de G9XXX Name agn? BK

**BK Bernie Bernie BK**

BK Thanks Bernie = Sri had QRM = Hr ANT is 2 el up 22 m es 1TT W = Wish I had ur 3 el = hr no space fer big ants = Wx hr also fine temp 26 C = hv bn ham 1 yr, still getting used to cw = condx rotten past few days = hv hrd vy few stns on 40 m = only sum W6 on LP b4 sunset = hvnt had much luck wrking them tho = ok must run hv to do sum chores in the house = 73 cul bernie AR
G9YYY de G9XXX AR SK CL

**G9XXX de G9YYY OK Chris = Yes 3 el lot of fun = Wrk W6 on LP all the time = Condx**
**rotten hr too but wrked FO stn on SP at sunset = OK 73 tnx QSO es QSL via buro =**
**G9XXX de G9YYY SK**

Notice how the term "BK" was used to quickly pass the transmission back to the other station. This short QSO was reasonably chatty, but it assumes knowledge of the abbreviations, plus also some knowledge of DX calls and propagation. Also, note that Chris gave his power as 1TT W, using "cut" numbers, a T for a 0. This is quite common.

### Example 2 (a directional CQ):

CQ OC de G9BBB CQ OC de G9BBB G9BBB OC KN

**de IK1XYZ**

CQ OC de G9BBB CQ OC de G9BBB G9BBB OC KN

**de IK1XYZ**

IK1XYZ pse qsy ur not in OC = CQ OC de G9BBB CQ OC de
G9BBB G9BBB OC KN

Note the KN at the end of a directional call to Oceania. The IK is just trying it on, he knew that G9BBB was calling OC only, but tried anyway, not very good operating. He should have respected that directional call.

**Example 3** (*a complete contest-style QSO*):

CQ TEST G9ZZZ G9ZZZ

**G9VVV**

G9VVV 5NN 13N

**5NN TT1**

TU G9ZZZ TEST

In contests, ending signals, the "DE" and other niceties are generally dispensed with. Notice how the example QSO includes no ending signals, and no instances of the "DE" signal. All contesters are aware of what is going on. Note the cut numbers again.

**Example 4** (*planning for your first QSO*):

For your first few contacts, write down everything you are going to send, in advance. When the other stations sends, just write down what he/she is sending. Keep the abbreviation list handy. Don't get too adventurous initially; just stick to the standard script until you find your feet. Here is a suggested first QSO:

QRL?
CQ CQ CQ de G9RRR G9RRR AR PSE K

**G9RRR DE G9PPP G9PPP AR PSE KN**

G9PPP de G9RRR GM = Name Bill QTH HULL = UR RST 599 =
This is my 1st QSO on CW HI = G9PPP de G9RRR AR KN

**G9RRR de G9PPP OK Bill = all OK = UR RST 579 579 = Name is Sid Sid es
running 100 W to a dipole = Hw? =
G9RRR de G9PPP AR KN**

After the initial couple of overs, you can either finish if you are nervous, or carry on. If the other station is a good operator he will slow down to your speed level and also take into account that it is your first CW QSO.

## Types of Morse Key

There are several types of key and keyer that can be used today, ranging from the traditional hand, or straight, key right through to highly sophisticated electronic keyers which use very complicated software and digital techniques.

Most modern transceivers have quite so-phisticated keying arrangements built in, including programmable macros or mem-ories, and automatically generated serial numbers for use in contests.

*Fig 5.5a: shows an early Vibroplex bug*

## The Straight Key

This is the traditional Morse key using a le-ver and an up/down movement and is the usual starting point when learning to send. The technique of using this key has been de-scribed in an earlier chapter. There are literally hundreds of different designs over the decades that Morse has been around and it is fascinating to look at some of them, You can find lots of pictures on the Internet, and there are also dedicated museums around. Indeed collecting Morse keys is a hobby in its own right.

## The Side Swiper

A form of key that uses a side to side movement to make and break the contacts. Most were made from steak knives, hacksaw blades or similar. This type of key requires par-ticular skill to attain good Morse. They are also known as 'cooties'.

## Semi-automatic mechanical key

Also called a 'bug', this is a mechanical key with a 'paddle' used by the operator. It has a weighted arm to automatically make a series of dots when the paddle is pressed to the right. These were adjustable in speed by moving the weight along the arm. **Fig 5.5**a shows an early Vibroplex bug. You can clearly see the weight on the arm to adjust the speed of sending. You have to make your own dashes by pressing the paddle to the left. McElroy and Eddystone made some early ones; **Fig 5.5**b shows a Vibroplex paddle.

## Electronic Keyer

Used with an external 'paddle', these have the ability to automatically create dots and dashes. Like the bug, the electronic keyer operates sideways. When pressed to one side the electronics generate a series of 'dahs' and when pressed the other way, a series of 'dits'. Most electronic keyers include a dit memory function which frees the operator from the need to perfectly time his transitions in the sequence dah-dit-dah. With dit memory, if the operator's keying action is about one dit

*Fig 5.5b: Modern Vibroplex paddle key*

ahead of the actual transmission, the keyer's output for each letter will be machine-perfect. An iambic keyer sports dual paddles, one for dit and one for dah; pressing both at the same time produces an alternating dit-dah-dit-dah sequence. Electronic keyers allow very high speed transmission of code.

## Morse keyboards and generators

A variety of electronic based products that use digital technology to generate Morse code. These days, for the utmost efficiency, most people use computers for logging, duping, scoring and sending, so touch typing is a useful skill.

## Using an electronic keyer and paddle

Anything over 20 wpm will be difficult to maintain on the straight key, and although it is possible to key around 25 wpm with the straight key, it is much easier with an electronic keyer

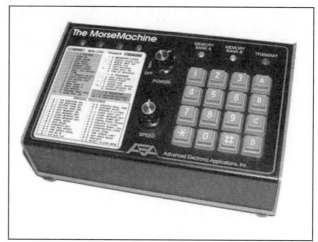

*Fig 5.6: AEA MM-3 keyer*

and paddle. Most transceivers have electronic keyers built in and you could manage with that and a paddle. However, I prefer an external keyer, for two reasons. One is that it can be used to key other transceivers with the same memory functions, plus all the other options that external keyers have. The other is that it has more versatility in some situations, such as contesting with a computer, and practising off the air.

I have an AEA MM3 Morse Machine, and have used that for around 15 years now. *See* **Fig 5.6** Prior to that I had a home-made TTL memory keyer that I built myself. The MM3 has a super side-tone, something that is very important to a CW operator, and also lots of pre-programmable memories that have various uses. It also

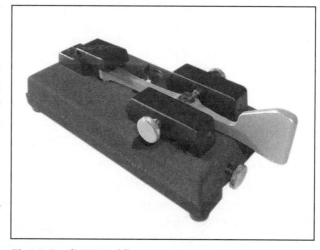

*Fig 5.7: Begali HST Paddle*

has a Doctor DX feature, a QSO and pile-up contest feature, and these can be very useful for off-air practice. The paddle I use is Vibroplex single lever paddle that I bought around 40 years ago, and it is still going strong! **Fig 5.5** If I tell you I bought it for £6 brand new, that should tell you how long I have had it! Unfortunately they are a bit more than that now.

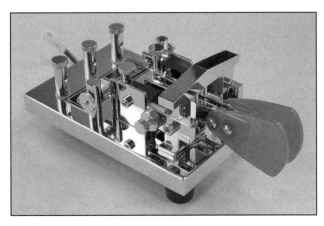

*Fig 5.8: Twin Paddle by Toshihiko Ujile*

Have a look at paddles and try several before you decide what to buy. I cannot use a double lever paddle at all, having been brought up with the single lever. I have just changed my allegiance and now have a Begali HST paddle and prefer that now (*See* **Fig 5.7**). However, starting from scratch, the Iambic might be a better one to have. There are several different types made so try them all before deciding. The twin Lever Paddle by Toshihiko Ujileis shown in **Fig 5.8** changing to this method will again require lots of practice before you use it on the air, but it will allow you to build up your speed to 40 wpm plus if you practice enough.

## What does Iambic mean?

Dual lever paddles are sometimes referred to as "iambic paddles". This is a misnoma inasmuch that a dual lever paddle can be used with a normal keyer and used in the normal way. In order to operate in iambic mode, the keyer itself must be an iambic keyer. An iambic keyer will send an alternating sequence of dits and dahs as long as both the dit and dah switches are depressed or squeezed.

An iambic keyer is normally used with a dual lever paddle. It consists of two separately actuated switches. As I am right handed I use my thumb for the dits and index finger for the dahs. You can also use a single lever paddle with an iambic keyer but

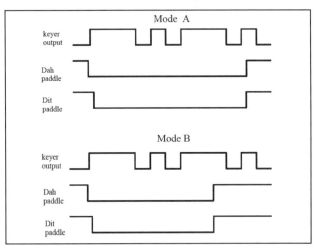

*Fig 5.9: Iambic modes A and B compared (from What's all this iambic keyer mode A and B stuff, anyhow? by Chuck Olson, WB9KZY)*

you won't be able to take advantage of the iambic properties of the keyer. Single lever keying is sometimes called slap keying since you can only depress either the dit (slap to the right) or dah (slap to the left) switch – you can't depress both at the same time.

## Iambic A or Iambic B?

The difference between mode A and B lies in what the keyer does when both paddles are released. The mode A keyer completes the element being sent when the paddles are released. The mode B keyer sends an additional element opposite to the one being sent when the paddles are released. You can tell the basic difference between the modes with the letter C. In mode A you could squeeze both paddles (dah before dit) and you would let go of both after hearing the last dit. With mode B, you start the same BUT let go of both paddles after hearing the second *dah*. The diagram in **Fig 5.9** shows a letter C being sent with mode A and with mode B.

Think carefully about buying your paddle before actually making the purchase. Looking at my music analogy again, a child learning the piano and using an el cheapo piano bought at the local auction, on which some notes work, others don't and the keys have half the tops missing, will have no inspiration at all in learning, and even less in practicing. If that child has a very nice piano, in tune, tuned regularly every year, simple music will sound nice and the child will be inspired. It's the same with a paddle. Don't buy the cheapest one around. It must be heavy, have a solid mechanical action and even look nice. The contacts should be gold plated and adjustments should be on a micro thread so that you can adjust the gap down to a minimum.

Starting from scratch it is probably advisable to buy a double lever paddle and learn the Iambic way. A few interesting statistics here might sway you.

These figures are taken from an article written by Charles Adams K7QO in a long article that is very worthwhile reading: *http://www.morsex.com/pubs/iambicmyth.pdf*

Here are the number of strokes it takes to send each letter using a straight key.

> One Stroke --- E and T
>
> Two Strokes --- A, I, N, and M
>
> Three Strokes --- K, O, S, U, W, R, D, and G
>
> Four Strokes --- B, C, F, H, J, L, P, Q, V, X, Y, and Z
>
> Five Strokes ---- 1, 2, 3, 4, 5, 6, 7, 8, 9, and 0

So if you were to send the entire alphabet and all the numerals you would have to work the key a total of 2 + 8 + 24 + 48 + 50 which is 132 key closures.

No wonder it is tiring work sending a long session with a straight key.

Now let's try the old 'bug' key. Historically the bug was invented before we had digital electronics. In a way, it's a shame that it has died a death, because with a bug you could usually tell who was sending. There was still "character" in the Morse, much as with the straight key.

One Stroke --- E, I, S, H, 5, T

Two Strokes --- A, B, D, M, N, 6, U, V, 4, 6

Three Strokes --- F, G, K, L, O, R, W, X, Z, 3, 7

Four Strokes --- C, J, P, Q, Y, 2, 8

Five Strokes --- 9, 0

Again, totaling up the number of strokes we get 6 + 20 + 33 + 28 + 10 giving us the winning number of 87 motions. This is quite a savings over 132 strokes required for the straight key. Timing-wise it gave the operator considerable more accurate timing on the dits, even if they did fade eventually!

There is still a limit of human capabilities to send by hand each long element.

Then along came the first electronic keyer. My first one was the OZ7BO keyer using two 12AT7 valves and high speed keying relays. No memory or fancy internal storage, just a plain two valve keyer that timed the dit and the dah well.

Now let's again go through our counting exercise but this time using only a single lever paddle used with an electronic keyer. There are still lots of good ops using a single lever paddle. I still use one myself.

Here is the count using the single lever paddle.

One Stroke --- E, H, I, M, O, S, T, 0, and 5

Two Strokes --- A, B, D, G, J, N, U, V, W, Z, 1, 2, 3, 4, 6, 7, 8 and 9

Three Strokes --- F, K, L, P, Q, R, X, Y

That saved a lot. Totaling up we get 9 + 36 + 24 for a total of 69 which again is a reduction from the previous two methods that involved 132 and 87 strokes for their respective totals.

And lastly we have the dual Iambic paddles and more sophisticated keyers. Often referred to as 'squeeze' keying since the physical motion of the fingers is like squeezing the two paddles together in sending some of the characters. It matters not whether you are using mode A or mode B for the keyer.

One Stroke --- E, H, I, M, O, S, T, 0, and 5

Two Strokes --- A, B, D, F, G, J, K, L, N, Q, R, U,

V, W, Y, Z, 1, 2, 3, 4, 6, 7, 8 and 9

Three Strokes --- P and X

Now we have 9 + 48 + 6 for a total of 63 strokes with again a savings in strokes, but only about a 10 percent gain. It is enough, and we'll take all the help we can get. So look at the totals again 132, 87, 69, and 63 for each of the methods of sending Morse. With the Iambic Keying you can save over 50 per cent of the work of using a straight key.

## Ultimatic keying

The difference between iambic and Ultimatic keying is that when you hold down both paddles, the Ultimatic keyer sends a series of elements corresponding to the last paddle closed instead of sending alternate dits and dashes as an iambic keyer would.

For example, the sequence L (Left) on, R (Right) on would cause an iambic keyer to send di-dah-di-dah..... An Ultimatic keyer would, however, send di-dah-dah-dah.

If you count the number of paddle movements, you can see where this might be advantageous. There's no advantage when sending a K. The sequence is R on, L on, L off, R off for both iambic and Ultimatic keyers. Take X, however. When using iambic keying, it's R on, R off, L on, L off, R on, R off. With Ultimatic keying, the number of paddle movements is the same as for the iambic - R on, L on, L off, R off. - a savings of two paddle movements. You just hold down the left paddle a little longer for the X then for the K.

## The Touch Paddle

Recently developed is the touch paddle, with no moving parts at all, relying on the capacitive effect, the slightest touch on the paddle is all that is needed. Peter Raven G4KLM produces a very nice paddle and keyer **Fig 5.10**. They have proved very popular and are very competitively priced. Several local amateurs have them and have discarded their old paddle in favour of this new one. They are quite heavy too, which is very desirable. The keyer shown in

*Fig 5.10: Touch Paddle by Peter Raven G4KLM*

**Fig 5.11** has its own in-built paddle, but Peter is producing another model without the paddle.

Touch Key dimensions, 110x65x40 mm Weight 550g

Memory Keyer 135x130x51 mm

Touch Key runs on 2x AA cells, under normal operating conditions should last approx two years. 12 V model also available with 3.3 regulator on board. All components are surface mount.

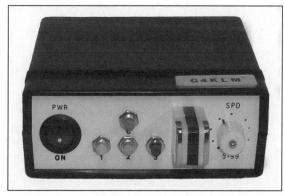

*Fig 5.11: Touch Paddle and Keyer by Peter Raven G4KLM*

The Memory Keyer is based on the K1EL K14 chip. This runs on a 9V PP3 battery, and also has a 12 v input. Up to six messages can be programmed in.

If you are interested in either of these, contact Peter at:
*peter@zs757.plus.com*

Learning to use a paddle, whatever type you choose, again can be compared to the playing of the piano. I like to quote the response that John Lill the concert pianist gave to a reporter after his playing of the Rackmaninov 3rd piano concerto. The reporter said, "Mr Lill, you ARE lucky to be able to play like that" His response was: " Yes, and do you know, the harder I practice, the luckier I seem to get". John Lill is also a licensed amateur, although I have never been able to find out his call sign!

Using a paddle is the best way of using CW on the air with maximum comfort and minimum effort and is used by all good CW operators. Of course, you could take it even further and throw away the key altogether and use a computer keyboard if you can touch type! This is cheating in some ways, avoiding the skill of using a paddle for everyday use, but is used in DX-peditions and contests, because of the time saved and the accuracy obtained over the human being sending it. Love it or loathe it, you cannot halt progress!

# Chapter 6

# Progress at Last

By this time, you will have devoted enough time and patience to become proficient at both receiving and sending with an electronic keyer at around 15-20 wpm. Listening on the HF bands has revealed that conversations are taking place, not merely an exchange of dots and dashes, and you are enthusiastic enough to want to work some DX. Obviously you have mastered all the abbreviations too. You will have had lots of QSOs on the air at a speed you can manage comfortably, in order to gain experience in doing just that. When you feel completely at ease with this, it is time to take the next step.

In this chapter you will have a whole new learning curve. If you want to be a really good operator, just as you thought the practice was all over, well here's news for you! It isn't!

## Build a keyer from a kit

The photograph shown in **Fig 6.1** shows a memory keyer produced by Peter Raven G4KLM, who also makes the touch paddle described in the previous chapter. The one shown in the picture has a built-in touch paddle, but of course for the home constructor this is not essential. The paddle can be external and to suit the individual. It is relatively easy to construct and is based on the new K16 chip from the K1EL website. It has a huge command set and is extremely versatile. In fact there are 26 Immediate commands available and 13 Extended commands. Peter says that if anybody is interested in building it, he would be prepared to offer advice.

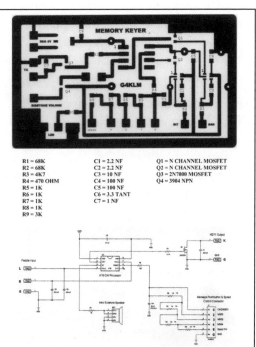

*Fig 6.1: Memory Keyer Layout*

The circuit board layout, diagram and component list is shown below:

- The memory keyer enclosure is from RS Components Part no 119-8912
- The Touch Key enclosure also from RS Part no 838-524
- All components available from RS –except:
- Push switches pots and knobs obtained from China
- PCB design with RS Design Spark Software (Free)
- K16 chip from the K1EL website. $8 with $10 postage it is also available in surface mount.

## Practice Your Sending

Use a bug, or preferably an electronic iambic keyer and paddle set up. The electronic keyer sends "perfect" CW characters, spacing and rhythm, a big help in your mental training activity.

Adjust the paddle to a very light action. You don't want to be slapping the key all about the table top! Good paddle keys are heavy for this reason. If it is sliding on the desk, you can now buy a sticky-pad from most car accessory shops for about £5. It is a piece of plastic that retains its sticky properties. It will stick to the desk like glue, and the key will stick to it. It is completely removable and washable, because after a time it attracts dust and loses some of the stickiness. With washing, this is soon restored. There are other solutions too. One that is quite common is an orange lattice material, which does a similar job.

Now begin practice to send quickly. This sending practice also works wonders on the way to becoming a QRQ operator. Why? Because, now you must form words to express ideas in your mind, while simultaneously sending the thoughts out as CW. This inverts what has been going on in your mental processes to receive CW. As you increase your speed ability, you will not even be thinking "letter to CW" translation, but will be mentally and automatically sending CW as if it were another language with which you have become quite comfortable.

Your mind will be training on CW in such a way that when it can send fast, it will use the same subconscious patterns to also receive fast. There is no short cut method to this; you just have to sit there for a few hours practising. Sorry if I keep repeating this, but really there is no substitute.

Try to arrange a few skeds with friends at the same level, and spend a few hours a week on the key just chatting. Eventually this will seem just as good as normal voice communications. Gradually increase your speed and keep the competition going, this is a good way to get through the 30 wpm and even 40 wpm barriers. After that it becomes a problem sending, even with a paddle! Some amateurs have abandoned the paddle in preference to a keyboard.

Above all, do try to have a few CW contacts each day. Don't rest on your laurels, thinking that once you have attained a good speed that it will remain with you. Even a top notch concert pianist still practices for several hours each day. Pick a few contests to try, just taking part will hone your skills very well, and you will find that using a keyer and log book really is slow compared to those using a computer. Time to change again.

## Operating contests

There is more to encourage you to practice. In order to become a proficient contest operator, you now have to learn how to touch type on a computer keyboard. Hopefully, especially in these days when computers are common place, you will have this skill already. I taught myself on an old upright typewriter in the – well never mind when! All contests are run using a computer program now; it would not be possible without them, at least not to be competitive. Several decades ago, logging itself was a skill, assisting the operator to maintain a good Q rate, but it is far too slow by modern standards.

Of course, there's nothing to prevent you using a key - even a straight one -in a contest if you simply want to improve your technique and speed, rather than compete with the 'big guns'.

Contesters use computer logging programs which do most of the transmitting for them, as well as the log tasks and duplicate checking; some programs do even more! But to use them efficiently to contest, you have to be a pretty good keyboard operator as well, and also know the use of the function keys, without using crib notes or key overlay guides during the 'test. By learning to touch-type, rather than using just two fingers, your typing skills will be able to keep up with, and surpass, your Morse skills. This will be an advantage when running a contest or pile-up enabling you to drink your tea or eat a sandwich at the same time.

The RSGB Cumulative events are good for beginners in CW contesting. These take place on a weekday evening, and are only 90 minutes long. If it is your first time in a contest, there is a slow section at the top end of the CW band which caters for beginners and the inexperienced. Good operators will slow down to your speed and have a bit of patience in order to encourage more use of the bands.

## Computer Programs for Morse

These are many and varied. They range from the very basic to ones that have a WOW factor, enabling you to simulate a contest divorced from the radio, but with all the reality of using one. You can use training programs to keep up your receiving skills. I teach Morse and I use several programs here. You have lots to choose from however – try a search on the Internet.  Below is a selection.

First of all, however, is a program that will allow you to cheat!  I am not advocating this on a permanent basis, but it has helped a few in our Club to taste the excitement of operating CW without actually being able to copy anything. I am talking about:

**CWget** - This is a program that can be run together with a computer logging program, such as N1MM, and enable the unskilled operator to run a CW contest and achieve a reasonable score. Go to the download page: *http://www.dxsoft.com/en/products/cwget/*

This program will enable you to decode Morse code (CW) via a sound card to text. It can also work as a narrow-band sound DSP-filter. No additional hardware is required, just a receiver and a computer with a sound card. It will receive the CW and N1MM will transmit it, as usual. One of our Club members scored 59 Qs using this method.

I have not used this program at all, for obvious reasons, I do not need it! However, despite saying what I have said above, about using it to enter a contest, please don't become reliant on it, especially when trying to use CW for other, everyday contacts. You cannot possibly have the same sense and comprehension that a normal CW operator has and it can lead to all sorts of problems. Using it for basic contest exchanges is fine, but nothing can emulate a human brain and the brain is the only way to decode CW used in QSOs, Nets, chasing DX etc. When you become a proficient CW operator, you will understand what I mean.

**AA9PW** - For basic practice: *http://www.aa9pw.com/radio/morse.html*
This has groups of letters, numbers, mixed characters, punctuation, pro-signs, call signs and a mixture of all the above. It also has a News Feed that converts to Morse. I find it very useful. The Morse practice page is shown and explained in Chapter 3.

**TEACH4** - *www.nzart.org.nz/exam/index.html*
For a different tone and general practice: Morse Teaching Program by ZL1AN.

This can be found on the AC6V Morse Page, along with many others. There is a screen shot of Teach4 in Chapter 4, together with an explanation.

**RufzXP** - *http://rufzxp.software.informer.com/*
This program is ideal for practicing receiving call signs. These usually present a problem and attention has to be paid to overcoming any difficulties with them. View them as mixed groups, and these days call signs are anything but a standard format! This program sends you a block of 50 calls in one session. It starts nice and slowly, but if you receive correctly it will gradually speed up. It obviously finds your Achilles heel and if you make a couple of mistakes, it slows down again! It is great fun to use and you can enter your call into a leaderboard too. It does become very addictive however in your quest to copy even more calls and increase your score each time, but then that is the idea of encouraging you to practice!

**WinMorse 2** (*www.winmorse.com*):
This is a very versatile program and has a number of very useful utilities with it. You can convert text files to Morse and save them on your computer for use in practice at any time. You can set the Farnsworth to 25WPM and try speeds varying from basic 5 to 25WPM.

Both these programs utilise the Farnsworth method.

**Morse-runner** - For advanced practice: *http://www.dxatlas.com/MorseRunner/*
This program is ideal for using off air as a contest simulator. Written by Alex Shovkoplyas, VE3NEA, who also wrote DXAtlas, it is a lookalike for N1MM, with a very similar

layout. Speed, pitch and receiver bandwidth are all adjustable, and also programmable are QRM, QRN, QSB, and flutter, together with the amount of stations calling at any one time. It is very realistic, and is superb for handling pile-ups and this program too can be very addictive! You can download an audio file of someone running a pile-up and there is a league table of those having the highest scores. It is ideal for preparing for a CW contest and honing your operating skills, digging a call out of the QRM and so on. The screen shot, **Fig 6.2**, shows how similar it is to N1MM

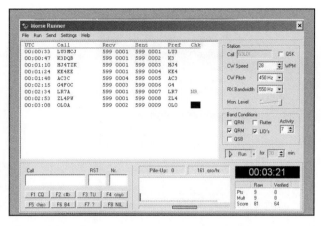

*Fig 6.2: Morse-Runner*

Alex has written another similar contest practice program, this time called:

**Pile-up Runner**
This is similar to Morse Runner, but is more for those who ARE the DX. It is intended as training to handle a pile-up from a DX location. Again, it is very addictive and very realistic, so be prepared for some action!

I think it could be confusing to mention even more, but if you do a Google search on the Internet, you can be sure to find one to please you.

## Computer programs for contesting

Try to visit a local amateur running one of the modern Contest programs, such as Writelog, Wintest, N1MM, EI5DI, Winlog, etc. Have a look at all of them. I have, and have settled on N1MM. It is freeware and is updated regularly. It also covers all the contest modes very nicely.

**Fig 6.3** shows a screen shot from N1MM after having been set up. Contest programs are more complex than Morse Practise programs and it is not possible to describe setting up any one of the above programs here. However, they are all in general use and there will be plenty of help available when you try to install one. It would be advisable to obtain that help in the first instance before trying to install it yourself. This particular screenshot shows N1MM set up for an RSGB CC CW contest. Two QSOs have already been logged and the partial entry shows G3Y and the possibilities of the call in the Check window. A bandmap is also shown but as it is not live there are no calls showing. Normally there would be lots of calls listed on the bandmap, and clicking on the call takes you onto that station's frequency ready for you to call him. Once set up, N1MM is

*Fig 6.3: Screen Shot of N1MM*

a very versatile contest program and one I would recommend to anybody starting. It might seem complex at first, but after a few contests it really is easy to operate.

Our local Club used to use SD, the contest program written by EI5DI. This is a simple CW program that doesn't have the bells and whistles of the likes of N1MM and WL. However, it worked on NFD for us for a number of years. Now, however, we have an increasing interest in Morse and have managed to steer most people onto N1MM. There are a few using other programs, including HRD.

## Clubs and Newsletters

If you operate a lot of CW on the HF bands, you may receive a very nice unsolicited surprise through the post one day. If you are a good operator, send good Morse, and are willing to talk to others on Morse, rather than have rubber-stamp contacts, you could be in line for membership to the A-1 Ops Club. You receive a membership certificate, like an award, membership details, with some cards which you can use to sponsor another operator. This is all done without soliciting for membership and without your knowledge so it adds to the pleasure when you receive your certificate.

You can also join the FOC, if you are lucky enough! This is the First Class Operator's Club and they have a limited membership, so you might have to wait a while!

You can join FISTS, the International Morse Preservation Society. They have a regular Newsletter and regular operating calling frequencies, activities, printed log-books and so on. FISTS is a very useful club to belong to, especially for the beginner. Their motto indicates their priority " Accuracy transcends speed, courtesy ar all times". Members will willingly slow down to your speed and make you feel comfortable. They have lots of on-air activities and events and you can join in as and when you get time. There are awards to be gained too, giving you incentive to get on the air even more!

There are others, so as you see Morse is far from dead, and in fact it will never die within the Amateur Radio Hobby.

In what follows, both CW and keyboard skills will be addressed.

## QRQ Receiving Practice

While waiting to acquire and set up some of the practice programs, do on-the-air receiving practice. Find QSOs in progress at a speed you can comfortably pencil/pen
copy. Now, put the pen/pencil down, and just start listening. Yes, try to recognize the
letters as they come along, and group them into words on your minds "blackboard".

Not easy to do, but keep trying anyway. It is going to take awhile, maybe even three or
four weeks before you can follow these easy speed QSOs in your head without writing
everything down! Jot down the call, the ops name, QTH and report, while just listening
to the rest.

While doing this, if you can find a willing friend, there is a way to augment this sort
of practice completely away from CW. Have your friend/spouse/relevant-other spell
words from a story or newspaper article to you! He is to read the story to you, but
not the word sounds, but spelling the words to you out-loud. This is what is going
on when one is "reading CW in his head"; words are being spelled to you "out-loud",
and you must form these spelled words into meaningful thoughts. Start at, one letter/
word space every second sounded by your helper. Have a letter spoken every tick of the
clock. This is a speed of 12 wpm (at the Paris standard, of 100 letters/workspaces per
minute equaling

20 wpm CW speed). Tune in WWV to get exact beats every second.

When you have no trouble forming the thoughts of the story/article in your mind as
the words are spelled to you at this rather slow pace, and then have your friend double
his rhythm, that is, two letters/word spaces per second spoken two per tick. This, of
course, doubles your word reading rate to 24 wpm. A big jump for CW, but not for
learning to read words spelled out to you in clear, plain English!! When you know the
story comfortably at this rate, your actual in the head CW reading speed should be
close behind, and you may be well on your way to QRQ operation.

At QRQ, you will be receiving letters/word spaces at 3 per second at a 36 wpm CW rate.

Maybe your friend can get the rhythm going at 3 letters/spaces per clock tick, and you
will know exactly what 36 wpm CW sounds like, this is a typical QRQ DX and contest
operation speed. Of course, using a musician's metronome would allow you to exactly
set the number of beats per minute; 20 wpm being 100 beats, 36, 180 per minute, 50
wpm, 250 letters/spaces, etc. My mechanical metronome has a highest beat rate of 208
per minute, or a bit over 41 wpm.

**W1AW On-line**

This is a good way of practicing plain language text. W1AW still transmits on the HF bands but also has a large number of MP3 files stored on line. Go to: *http://www.arrl. org/code-practice-files*

These files vary from 5 wpm up to 40 wpm. They make an excellent way of not only just increasing you copying speed, but also transferring it to the keyboard. I copy these files into Notepad and find this a very good way to increase copying ability at high speed.

Computer aided CW training programs are available. They will send code groups, random words, text and typical QSOs. They are all advertised, nearly monthly, in the ham magazines. Morse Academy is good, as is Code Master V. All of the included CW tests which come with MA can be sent by the computer at very high speeds, not just the speeds intended. Of course, they don't last long at high speed, but are very helpful for in-the-head CW reading practice. Using Code Master V, you can input via the keyboard, or text (.txt) file input, kilobytes of text for very long high speed CW listening practice runs.

I have taken lots of long text files directly from various Internet sites, and copied it directly into a CM V text file for this sort of high speed practice. I edit out a lot of punctuation marks from the text; I don't want to learn or know the code for quotation signs, semicolons, etc.!

## Using the Computer for Practice

The apparent purpose by the authors of MA and CM V is to teach the code, from A on up to text speed, assuming you want to use the keyboard to copy what is received. So if you really want to write down what is being received, then by all means use these programs to build up your keyboard skills, ear to key stroke response, to copying behind.

These programs can do that for you, just fine! But I will show you how to use them to get up to 50 wpm, copying in your head.

Now that you have CM V or MA, or another, here is how to use it to become QRQ qualified.

We are still talking about methods to read the code mentally, not writing or typing anything down as you receive it. That comes later.

With lots of CW text available in the computer program, you are ready to begin. Once you have determined your present 100% comfortable hand copying speed using pencil or pen, set your computer program to send clear text at about 5 wpm faster than your hand copying speed. Turn on the sending of the text at this speed, sit back, and just listen for 30 minutes, twice per day. First you will only be catching a letter every now and then; when you do, you will, without effort, congratulate yourself. While this happens, you will miss the next several letters! But keep at it. Soon you will get all the letters of a single word, again congratulations as you say the word to yourself, and again a lot of letters/words go on by, unrecognized!

But you are making progress. In a couple of weeks, or so, especially if you were able to get a friend to spell the words of stories/text to you, you will be able to understand the text being sent. As soon as you do, increase the speed another 5 wpm. Keep it up, and in 3 or 4 months, you may be up to 40 or more wpm! Try it, it works, and you will be amazed.

## How to use your CW skills to enhance your DX potential.

There is a world-wide beacon network that transmits 24/7 on CW at three different power levels. Monitoring these can give you an idea of just what propagation is like.

### Beacons and Reverse Beacons

#### NCDXF/IARU Beacons

On the 14, 18, 21, 24 and 28MHz amateur bands are a chain of propagation beacons that were constructed by and operated by the Northern California DX Foundation (NCDXF). The chain consists of 18 beacons which are time synchronised and follow a strict transmission schedule. Because of this it is possible to know at any given time which beacon is transmitting. Also because of this time synchronised schedule it has been possible to develop software that takes advantage of this. One such program is the well known BEACONSEE. This program can be setup in a number of ways to monitor the beacons on a given band or to monitor a single beacon across selected bands (provided you have a radio that is capable of being controlled by the computer). Using this program it is easy to see if propagation exists to a given part of the world, or what areas a particular band is open to (or just opening/closing). The beacon network has been carefully selected and the 6 main continents are represented.

All the beacons run the same equipment and antennas (which I believe are modified Kenwood TS50's and Cushcraft R5 Verticals). The beacons have a useful secondary feature which is a stepped output level. The first tone and the call sign are sent at full power (100 watts), the next tone is sent at 10 watts, then 1 watt and the final tone is at 100mW. It is amazing just how many beacons can be heard at all power levels. The 100mW tone is 30dB down on the 100W carrier, which would equate to 5 s points on your signal meter (using the 'standard 6dB per s point' calibration.)

In practise though you will find that doesn't hold true as receiver s meters are usually not very linear in calibration, especially over such a wide frequency range. What you will find is that if the first tone is loud, the chances are you will be able to hear all power levels (providing the noise level at your station allows!).

Each beacon runs on a very slightly different frequency/offset, which is an aid to identification, particularly if there is noise present on the band.

The beacons in order of keying are:

4U1UN (USA, NY), VE8AT (CANADA), W6WX (USA, CA), KH6WO (HAWAII), ZL6B (NEW ZEALAND), VK6RBP (AUSTRALIA), JA2IGY (JAPAN), RR9O (RUSSIA), VR2B (HONG KONG), 4S7B (SRI LANKA), ZS6DN (SOUTH AFRICA), 5Z4B (KENYA), 4X6TU (ISRAEL), OH2B (FINLAND), CS3B (MADEIRA), LU4AA (ARGENTINA), OA4B (PERU), YV5B (VENEZUELA)

*Fig 6.4 A screen shot of the BEACONSEE program.*

**Fig 6.4** shows a screen shot of the program.

The program can be downloaded from: *www.coaa.co.uk/beaconsee.htm*

**Beacon Tracker** by W6NEK displays a map with the beacons shown on it. The highlighted one, the one flashing, is the beacon transmitting. In the case of the diagram, **Fig 6.5**, it is CS3B. There are a variety of menus and displays that can be selected. These menu selections allow you to customize the look and feel of the beacon tracker map display. You have full control of the LED beacon marker display, beacon call sign display, beacon 10-second activity, etc. This allows you to quickly configure HF Beacon Tracker map display to your liking.

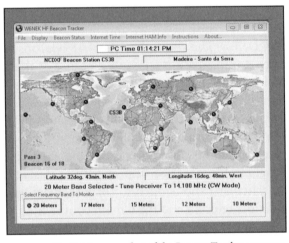

*Fig 6.5 A screen shot of the Beacon Tracker program.*

If everyone used the Beacons, there would be much more activity on the bands. What happens is that operators hear an empty band and assume propagation is poor or non existent. This happens most often on 15, 12, and 10 meters. As a matter of fact, this is the very reason the NCDXF/IARU International Beacon Network was established. To give Amateur Radio Operators a tool to measure band propagation independent of operator activity.

**The Reverse Beacon Network**

The Reverse Beacon Network is a revolutionary new idea. Instead of beacons actively transmitting signals, the RBN is a network of stations listening to the bands and reporting what stations they hear, when and how well.

You can see band openings in near-real time on an animated map. You can call a quick CQ, and see which reverse beacons hear you, and how strong you are. All you need do is transmit a quick CQ de G9zzz or TEST de G9zzz and then check to see how many stations have heard you, your signal strength and so on. You can even do relative checks and comparisons with other stations and see how your station compares. This not only checks propagation, but can also check your antenna for you against another one. It's a very useful tool and one that every CW operator should use.

Go to: *http://www.reversebeacon.net/*

Read about it and just see exactly what can be done. I think you will be hooked and definitely use this facility on a regular basis.

## CW Skimmer

CW Skimmer is a software package, available from Alex Shovkoplyas, VE3NEA, at www.DXAtlas.com. A 30-day full-featured trial version of release 1.1 is available free of charge. Combined with your current transceiver, or with Software Defined Radio (SDR) hardware that is already available, CW Skimmer will enable operators to be aware of everything that is going on across large swaths of any band. You can pick out individual signals and enhance their readability by putting them through a tight audio DSP filter, or click on a station and move your transceiver to its frequency, but what is truly different about Skimmer is its mega-multi-tasking decoders. It looks at the entire swath of spectrum it can "hear", identifies CW signals, and decodes them all. Meanwhile, it looks at the decoded text and works to identify stations newly arrived on the band, stations calling CQ, etc. It generates a time-stamped list of these stations and their frequencies, and makes them available via Telnet to your logging program or via the Internet to the hub server of the reverse beacon network (more on this below).

## Working the DX

You may well have caught the DX bug, now that you are a proficient CW operator! If that is the case, please remember to adhere to the DX Code of Conduct. You can download the complete resume here: *http://dx-code.org/iaru.html*

Or, just read the relevant information and try to behave as impeccably as possible on the air. There are many that don't and it is very tempting to admonish those that do make fools of themselves. Just ignore them and wait. They do go away eventually. There are always those around who wish to spoil other people's fun.

You can also download the booklet written by John Devoldere ON4UN and Mark Demeuleneere ON4WW, called Ethics and Operating Procedures for the Radio Amateur". It is available in more than 25 languages, so there are no excuses!

*http://www.ham-operating-ethics.org/versions.html*

# Operating Procedures

## A1-1. CW TUTORIAL

In addition to the quickie DXpedition and contest CW contacts, you can work a lot of DX in a one-on-one QSO. A lot of common DX is available on CW, with very little competition. For example, the mob will pileup on a European station on phone, but on CW on many occasions you can hear that same country calling CQ with no takers. An excellent CW Tutorial can be found by Jack Wagoner WB8FSV at URL: *http://www. netwalk.com/~fsv/CWguide.htm*

## Lets take it step by step

1   Have a list of CW Abbreviations, Prefixes, and Q-Signals handy. Some DX stations cannot converse in English but you both can get the essentials across with Q-Signals.

2   Know how to 'zero beat' a CW signal. Many stations have very narrow filters and you want to be in their bandpass. Refer to the operating manual for your radio.

3   Know how to use your RIT, XIT, Dual VFO's, and CW filters. *See* Chapter 2.

4   Listen for a DX station calling CQ or wait until they have finished with a QSO.

5   Good operators will send KN as a turn over, which is "go ahead, over, others keep out." Sending just K opens it for others to break in and this is OK if that is desired. SK is the signoff that should be used or CL ('clear') if closing your station.

6   Give a call in 1 X 2 call format -- DX11DX DE WZ9UUU WA9UUU AR (The AR is a prosign sent as one character, ie didahdidahdit and means that I am through with this transmission). The DX station knows their call, so send it once. Sending your call twice allows the other station to hear it, then confirm it.

7   If you make the connection, the usual follow up is his or her signal report, repeated twice if the contact is shaky and weak, then your name and QTH. Don't send more than that on the first round. Turn it back to the DX with a K or KN. This will allow the two of you to evaluate if a QSO is sustainable or desirable.

8   On the next over, ask about QSL information if you want it, before the band slips out.

9   If no DX is calling CQ, but the band seems open, find a clear frequency and listen for a bit, if clear, then send QRL? QRL asks is the frequency busy? If someone responds with C, or QRL, no need to respond and clutter up the frequency. If no response to your QRL, repeat a couple of times and then call CQ. Sending just QRL without your callsign is against the rules, but most do it anyway.

10  Calling CQ is typically in a 3 X 2 format  CQ CQ CQ   DE  WZ7UUU WZ7UUU   K.   Long long CQ's are likely to be ignored. Don't use AR instead of K as it means ending the transmission, and not an invitation for an answer. KN is a turn over to the station you are already working in a QSO

11  Listen for a few seconds using RIT to check for off frequency responses. If you have a narrow CW filter in line, use RIT and tune up and down from your transmit frequency to determine if someone is responding.

12  Repeat your CQ or QSY to a clear frequency, as you may be on a Big Gun frequency that can't hear you.

13  After the initial contact, it is typically DX11DX  DE  WX6DDD GM (GA, GE) OM TNX FER CALL UR RST ### (339, 599, 549, etc.) NAME HR IS ROD ROD. QTH IS SAN DIEGO, CA. SAN DIEGO, CA. HW? AR DX11DX  DE  WX6DDD K (OR) KN. See your list of abbreviations if you are not familiar with these.

14  DX11DX returns with essentially the same info, you may get ìRî indicating that DX11DX copied all, or QSL on all is sometimes sent.

15  The next round is an invitation to rag chew. If DX11DX is too fast for you, send a QRS (send slower please). Longer QSO's usually include your station configuration, the weather (WX), jobs, ages, etc. You may receive an invitation to operate QSK (break-in) where the QSO is much more conversational. Practice with a friend first as this takes some getting used to and proper equipment settings.

16  It is not necessary to do a (DX11DX   DE   WD6YYY) every time except every 10 minutes of course. When you turn it over ñ you can use BK or just KN or K.

17  A signoff looks like this:

DX11DX DE WF6TTT, FB VLAD TNX NICE QSO HPE CUL VY 73 GM SK DX11DX  DE  WF6TTT Use SK or CL (Closing Station) on your final transmission not AR or K (N)

18  Then there are some cuties signoffs dit dit, and a response of dit. Old Military types use dit dita dit dit (Shave and a Haircut) with the response of dit dit (2 Bits)!

19   For contests, a common CQ is 'test AC6V test'.

20   Tail-ending. Wait until another QSO is complete, and then call the station you want to contact.

21   Breaking into a QSO is not commonly done on CW and should be approached with caution. If it obvious that two old friends are in conversation, it is not advisable. If the exchanges include KN it's a signal that others are not welcome, best wait until the QSO is over and then tail-end. The standard break-in method on CW is to wait between transmissions and then send "BK" for break, or "BK de WT8III".

22   It is very common to send RST reports in abbreviated form, for example 599, is sent as 5NN. "N" in place of the number "9". Also another time saver is for the zero using a long "T". "T" is sent in place of the number zero as in " POWER HR IS 3TT WATTS". There is a number code for all numbers; however, the N and T codes are the most common ones.

23   Also CW stations sometimes report their zones as "A4" or "A5" instead of sending "14" or "15". 1 = A,  2 = U,  3 = V,  4 = 4,  5 = E,  6 = 6,  7 = B, 8 = D,  9 = N,  0 = T

## The Future

None of us knows what is in store, but if you had told me all this when I became licensed, in 1956, I would have thought it came straight out of the Eagle comic, probably the Dan Dare front page!   Having dated myself I wonder what another 55 years will bring, not that I shall worry about it, but I am very confident that CW will still be around!

I have tried to cover all I can think of that is associated with CW in this re-write. Hopefully I have not missed anything. Have fun, keep the practice up daily, hold daily CW QSOs; you will get there.  I am still working on it, but I am probably older than 90% of you!